CW00531018

Fundamentals of Ve

Fundamentals of Vehicle Bodywork

J. Fairbrother, TEng., LMIBE, MIBCAM

Chief Examiner, City and Guilds of London Institute,
  Vehicle Body Engineering Technicians
Senior Lecturer in Vehicle Body Crafts Studies and Body Engineering,
  Department of Automobile Engineering, Willesden College of Technology

Fairbrother

HUTCHINSON

London Melbourne Sydney Auckland Johannesburg

Hutchinson & Co. (Publishers) Ltd
An imprint of the Hutchinson Publishing Group
17–21 Conway Street, London W1P 6JD

Hutchinson Group (Australia) Pty Ltd
30–32 Cremorne Street, Richmond South, Victoria 3121
PO Box 151, Broadway, New South Wales 2007

Hutchinson Group (NZ) Ltd
32–34 View Road, PO Box 40–086, Glenfield, Auckland 10

Hutchinson Group (SA) (Pty) Ltd
PO Box 337, Bergvlei 2012, South Africa

First published 1981
Reprinted 1983

© J. Fairbrother 1981
Illustrations © Hutchinson & Co. (Publishers) Ltd 1981

Set in Times by Ebony Press

Printed in Great Britain by the Anchor Press Ltd
and bound by Wm Brendon & Son Ltd
both of Tiptree, Essex

British Library Cataloguing in Publication Data
Fairbrother, J
    Fundamentals of vehicle bodywork.
    1. Motor vehicles – Bodies
    I. Title

ISBN 0 09 144390 3 cased
        0 09 144391 1 paper

Contents

Preface

Fundamentals of Vehicle Bodywork is not meant to cover any particular syllabus as a whole, be it CGLI Vehicle Body Crafts Studies or TEC Vehicle Body Engineering. It does, however, deal with subject matter relevant to these and other motor vehicle courses and aims to develop an appreciation and broader understanding of Vehicle Bodywork, the recommended processes and procedures, performance characteristics, material requirements and considerations to ensure strength reliability, serviceability and safety.

After a substantial and vigorous, yet rewarding, apprenticeship as a wheelwright and carriage builder and motor body builder, industrial experience as a body builder and finisher of Passenger Service Vehicles and over twenty years of lecturing in Vehicle Body Craft Studies and Body Engineering, I would like to share my experiences and cumulation of lecturing notes so that students of motor body building may benefit, if only just a small portion, from this work.

I wish to thank the industries who have kindly permitted the use of their literature and the motor manufacturers for their guidelines on recommended procedure; the CGLI for permission to publish examination questions; Mr L. L. Allen, OBE, former Principal of Willesden College of Technology and Chairman of the CGLI 395–2–13/14 Moderation Committee, and other members, for their consideration and understanding of examination setting; Mr George Cross, FIBCAM, and Mr S McKinnon, formerly part-time lecturers at the Wigan and District Mining and Technical College for inspiring my interest in Vehicle Body Building.

ACKNOWLEDGEMENTS

Alcan Metal Centres Ltd
Anthony Carrimore (Sales) Ltd
Cargo Van Equipment Ltd
City and Guilds of London Institute
Crane Fruehauf Ltd
Duple Coachbuilders Ltd
Eurofont (UK) Ltd
Finnish Plywood Development Association

Ford Motor Company Ltd
Park Royal Vehicles
PLC Engineering Company Ltd
Ratcliffe Tail Lifts Ltd
Sound Service (Oxford) Ltd
TI Metsec Ltd
Vauxhall Motors Ltd

1 Brief history of the motor car

Factors that influenced development

For the majority of historians, the vital starting point, the basis of the modern car, was Cugnot's fantastic three-wheeled, steam-driven gun tractor, completed in 1765. But although France may claim Cugnot as the inventor of the motorized vehicle, he based his work on the principles of locomotion discovered by the Scotsmen, Watt and Murdock, and the Englishmen, Savery and Newcomen.

In the two ensuing decades it was Britain that effectively pioneered steam public service vehicles while Cugnot's clumsy invention led to his ruin.

Many of these early machines had carriage wheels, others had metal ones, and consequently the early history and development of the wheel is fundamental to the entire story of the motor car.

Inevitably the history of the motor car and of motoring through the ages is deeply influenced by contemporary political and economic events. An example is the unfortunate 1865 Act regulating locomotives on highways which has been mis-named the 'Red Flag Act'! Thus while other countries were rapidly developing bigger and better motor cars, it was still illegal to drive in Britain without a man with a flag walking in front of the car. Consequently, Britain lost years of leeway in automobilism which were not made up until the 'Emancipation' Act of 1896 was passed; that is why Daimler and Benz had a significant advantage over Simms, Lanchester and Austin.

The last quarter of the nineteenth century saw the beginnings of the great motor manufacturing corporations and the rise of Henry Ford. It also produced many strange inventions; the electric motor reached its zenith in France and America in the 1890s yet it became obsolete shortly afterwards. If the last years of the nineteenth century were formative ones, the beginning of the twentieth century showed clear evidence of the crystallization of design and of organised effort. Wild scrambles to earn colossal fortunes were nicely balanced by the need to produce increasingly efficient machines and this situation survives today – to the benefit of the customer.

From the very early days, the 'horseless carriages' and the real cars that evolved from them bred a spirit of friendly rivalry among enthusiasts. Safety lay only in the sheer bulk of the larger machines and in the restricted speed of the lighter ones. Punctures happened by the mile, dense dust clouds obscured vision, burning tar was a hazard in hot weather and brakes were unreliable.

The historic period from 1905 to 1920 also saw the inception of Britain's world-famous Tourist Trophy races in 1905, the Vanderbilt Cup series in America and in 1911 the first of the Indianapolis 500-mile races. After the First World War British manufacturers were among the first to recognize the general public's growing demand for motor cars and it was during this period that William Morris, the genius of the British motor industry, laid the foundations for the British Motor Corporation/Leyland colossus.

It was America, however, that led the world in the manufacture of popular cars. The Ford empire produced more than 15 million Model T cars in the nineteen years from 1908 on. But despite the First World War, manufacturers throughout the world, and particularly in Europe, made tremendous progress. In France, André Citroen presented a new challenge to the ancient Renault concern and in Italy no other manufacturer matched the business acumen and enthusiasm of Fiat.

Many enthusiasts of today consider that the most exciting years of motoring were in the 1920s; some of the finest designs and technical innovations stemmed from this era. It was between 1920 and 1925 that car manufacturers finally settled down to a standard technique of manufacture and this was to influence car building for many decades to come. While it must be remembered that such features as overhead camshafts, epicyclic gear boxes and coil ignition were far from new even in the 1920s, the fact remains that these improvements began to impress a wider public. In Britain public interest in motoring was continually stimulated by the enthusiasm of the Royal Family, which has continued to the present day. It was at this time that many of the great names and records were made. In 1926 a 9-litre single-seater Renault broke the 24-hour record at Montlbery covering 2600 miles at over 107 mile/h. A Duesenberg, the car that was the status symbol in the great days of Hollywood, won the 1924 Indianapolis contest; Bentleys also achieved spectacular success and a brief revival of the steam car produced the Doble which travelled at speeds of more than 100 mile/h.

On the industrial side, the manufacturers were beginning to feel the economic slump and this affected America's production first of all. Then, during the Second World War private motoring ceased. The great motor companies made military vehicles and even these were almost exclusively based on pre-war designs for civilian cars and lorries. It was Germany that produced at this time the basis of a family car that was later to gain enormous popularity as the Volkswagen.

In the first year of peace, the fiftieth anniversary of the motor car was celebrated, on the basis that 1895–1896 was the time when the first practical car was produced.

British manufacturers were among the first to resume production after the war, but the trade generally was disturbed by the world-wide political upheaval. A classic example of the tragic results of post-war intrigue was the arrest of Louis Renault who was accused of collaboration with the Nazis and died in prison under mysterious circumstances. His vast automobile empire was then taken under state control and expanded to meet global demand for its popular products.

With the improvement in the international situation there was a resurgence in the motor industry. America's greatest technological contribution was the perfection of automatic transmission and, in more recent years, American manufacturers have successfully invaded the international competition field with racing cars and land speed record machines, whilst their large, powerful engines are in great demand by European producers of GT cars. The French and Italians were also quick to see that competitions and track work were good for sales as well as development, but it took longer for British manufacturers to concern themselves with sport. Even the much publicised 'national' BRM racing car was the product of a small group of men with little financial backing; it took fifteen years for the name to attain success. However, the Jaguar was supreme in the sports-racing category and the racing world owes a great debt to the remarkable Sir William Lyons.

One of the most amazing aspects of recent automobile history is the rapid expansion of the Japanese motor industry, resulting in many economic and competitive problems for other motor manufacturers. The huge increases in fuel prices has led to 'common formula' small cars with very little difference performance-wise, initial price, running costs and availability seemingly being the main factors influencing sales.

The first motor car bodies made between 1896 and 1910 were similar in design to horse-drawn carriages and made almost entirely of wood. The coachwork was 'crude' since the design effort was concentrated on the engine and transmission. These early vehicles were known as 'horseless carriages' and manufactured by small individual firms in very small quantities and at great expense.

The credit for the first attempt at solving the problems of mass production is usually given to Henry Ford. The famous model T, launched in 1913 with the slogan 'A Car for Everyone', was the first mass-produced vehicle. Ford realized that while it took only about ten man-hours to assemble the engine, body manufacture took far longer and represented the main factor in the price of the car.

In 1920 the Budd Corporation in Philadelphia took out a patent for an all-metal body involving considerable welding. A wide range of tools and presses enabled all the components of the body to be made from sheet steel without much manual labour, thus resulting in cost reduction. The components were then assembled by either gas welding, drilling and bolting, or screws and rivets.

During the 1930s, the joining of sheet metal components was greatly simplified by the introduction of electric resistance (spot) welding. This process has advantages in that it does not cause any distortion and is a faster means of welding metal structures. The introduction of spot welding marked the start of true mass production of vehicles.

The next landmark in the development of body engineering was reached in the 1950s with the introduction of unit construction (combination of the chassis and body into an integral sheet metal structure – the body became a load-bearing structure of the car). Integral vehicles last longer due to their greater rigidity, require fewer parts and assembly operations and are more economical due to weight reduction.

Basic studies in the analysis of vehicle bodies as load-carrying structures were carried out and together with the large increase in car production during the 1950s, the architecture of the vehicle became, in many cases, more important, the popularity of the model being determined by the 'coachwork' The Italians led the field in styling and this led to the setting up of styling departments in the car-producing industries. Small firms grouped together and became large empires. The latest period in the history of vehicle bodies has been characterized by the search for new materials such as plastics, the need for safety motor vehicles and aerodynamic considerations for fuel economy and stability.

Great strides have been made in the evolution of the motor car since 1765 when Cugnot's steam wagon travelled at 4.8 km/h (3 mile/h) to the modern vehicle which carries passengers at speeds that at one time were thought to be beyond human endurance.

Historic language of the coachbuilder

There has never been a precise terminology to describe different kinds of bodywork or a way of differentiating among the kinds of vehicle for transporting drivers and passengers. There has always been some confusion in terms, particular words being employed at the same time to describe different kinds of cars and body styles; the same word has often meant different things to, say, an Englishman, a Frenchman, an American or an Italian and some confusion still remains. It is possible to detail a simple vocabulary for the period 1895 to 1915 to identify the various types of vehicle in use in that period. In alphabetical order, the terms are:

Berlina Rarely used before the First World War. In general it meant a closed, luxury car, often with a small window which permitted the occupants to see but barely to be seen.

Cab A term taken directly from the horse-drawn carriage vocabulary and used to define a vehicle in which two passengers were enclosed while the driver was situated some distance away, usually in front and unprotected. But there were also electric cabs with the driver seated high up at the rear.

Cabriolet A word used towards the end of the period to describe a car with collapsible hood, with two or four seats.

Coupé Originally a vehicle 'cut' by a glass division, fixed or movable, behind the front seats. The driving position was only partially protected by the roof whilst the totally enclosed rear was very luxurious.

Coupé-cabriolet or double-cabriolet A long vehicle the front part of which was designed as a coupé whilst the rear part had the collapsible hood of the cabriolet. There were often two supplementary seats.

Coupé–chauffeur A coupé with the driving

position completely covered by a fixed roof, which was an extension of the rear roof.

Coupé de ville   A coupé with the driving position completely open.

Coupé–limousine   A vehicle with a totally enclosed rear and with the front part closed on the sides only.

Double berlina   A lengthened berlina with the driving position enclosed but separated from the rear part of the vehicle.

Double landaulet   A lengthened landaulet with two permament seats plus two occasionals in the rear, and a driving position in front.

Double phaeton   A phaeton with two double seats, including that of the driver.

Double tonneau   A lengthened tonneau in which the front seats were completely separate from the rear.

Landau   A cabriolet limousine in which only the roof behind the rear windows was collapsible.

Landaulet or landaulette   A small landau with only two seats in the closed collapsible roof portion.

Limousine   A lengthened coupe with double lateral windows in the rear part.

Limousine–chauffeur   A limousine with the rear roof extended forward to cover the driving position.

Phaeton   A term again taken from the days of the horse-drawn carriage. In the early days of motoring, it described a light car with large spoked wheels, with one double seat and generally a hood.

Runabout   An open sporting type of vehicle, generally with only two seats and simple bodywork.

Skiff or cab–skiff   An open sports car with streamlined, light bodywork.

Tonneau   An open vehicle with a bench seat in front and a semi-circular seat behind. A part of the seat was built into the rear door.

'Glass' saloon   A large closed vehicle, generally similar to a double berlina but with very large windows.

Saloon   A vehicle with the driving seat inside the enclosed car with no separation from the rear seats.

Torpedo   A long sports vehicle with hood, which was attached to the windscreen.

Victoria   Another term derived from the era of horses. The Victoria was long and luxurious with a separate driving position and a large rear seat and was equipped with hoods and side screens.

Voiturette   Used to describe an early touring car with two seats only and no hood.

Wagon-saloon   A particularly luxurious saloon used in America for civic and other purposes.

2 Car body design

Terminology

All-metal construction Generally this applies to body shells of both private cars and light commercial vehicles in which the construction is in the form of steel pressings assembled by welding to form a fabricated unit.

Alloy A mixture of two or more metals with or without other metallic or non-metallic elements.

Back light A central window in the rear panel of a saloon body.

Body sill The panel directly below the bottom of the doors.

Bonnet The metal cover over the engine compartment.

Boot This is the compartment provided in a car body which takes the luggage and often the spare wheel and fuel tank. It may be at the front or rear of the body depending upon the engine location.

Bottom side The frame member of the base of the body extending along the full length of the main portion of the body.

Bulkhead A transverse support or assembly in a body structure.

Cant panel The curved section of the roof top running between the comparatively flat top and the rain channel or gutter.

Cant rail The longitudinal framing of the roof at the joint.

Centre pillar The centre vertical support of a four-door saloon, sometimes referred to as 'B-C' post.

Door skins Door exterior panels.

Door trim Door interior lining panel.

Drip moulding A roof gutter to direct water from door openings.

Extrude To draw into lengths.

Fender American term for wing.

Firewall Panel dividing engine compartment from passenger compartment.

Flange A reinforcement on the edge of a panel formed at approximately right angles to the panel.

Four-door Denotes the type of saloon body having four doors.

Headlining Material, cloth, PVC, etc., used to cover the inner surface of the car roof.

Heelboard Vertical board or panel under rear seat which forms the support for the seat cushion.

Hinge pillar A pillar on which the door swings open or closed.

Hood American term for bonnet.

Nearside The left-hand side of the vehicle as viewed from the driver's seat.

Offside The right hand side of the vehicle as viewed from the driver's seat.

Pillar A vertical support of a body frame.

Pillar face The front of a pillar visible when the door is opened.

Prototype An original model often used for evaluation purposes.

Quarter light   The window directly above the quarter panel.

Quarter panel   The side panel extending from the door to the rear end of the body including the rear wing.

Saloon   An enclosed car body not having a partition between the front and rear seats.

Scuttle panel   The panel between the bonnet and the windscreen.

Squab   The rear seat-back construction.

Sub-frame   Members to which the engine and front-end assembly are attached.

Tunnel   A raised floor-panel section for drive-shaft clearance.

Turret   American term for roof.

Wheel-arch   Panel forming the inner housings for the road wheels.

Classification

There are many ways in which motor cars may be classified or slotted into convenient groups for recognition. Much depends on such factors as the manufacturer, the make of the car, the car line, the series and the body type or style. Distinctive groups of passenger car bodies include:

1   Small-bodied, mass-produced cars.
2   Medium-bodied, mass-produced cars.
3   Large-bodied, mass-produced cars.
4   Specially built bodywork using the major components of mass-produced models.
5   High-quality 'coach-built' cars.
6   Modified mass-produced bodywork to give a standard production model a more distinctive appearance.
7   Classes of sports and GT bodywork either mass produced or specially built.
8   Estate cars.

Styling forms

The most popular style for passenger cars is the two- or four-door saloon (see Figure 1). It has a

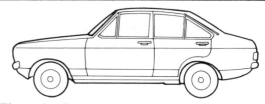

Figure 1   *Four-door saloon*

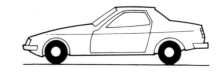

Figure 2   *Sports coupé*

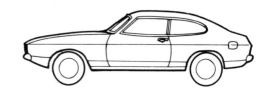

Figure 3   *Coupé*

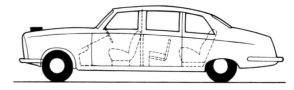

Figure 4   *Limousine*

Figure 5   *Estate car*

Figure 6   *Convertible*

fully enclosed, fixed-roof body for four or more people and no partition between the driver and the rear passengers. This type also has a separate luggage compartment.

Other styling forms include the sports coupé (Figure 2), a two-seater sports car with a fixed roof, and the coupé (Figure 3), which is similar in body style to the sports coupé, but has two small extra seats at the rear (thus it is often referred to as a 'two-plus-two').

The limousine (Figure 4) is characterized by a partition between the driver and the rear passengers and the high quality of the equipment and finish.

The estate car (Figure 5) has the roof extended to the rear to give more luggage space and goes under various names such as universal, kombi, station wagon, or camping brake.

The convertible (Figure 6) has a folding roof (hood) and wind-up windows, together with fully enclosed or open bodywork.

The Roadster has been described as a two-seater sports car with a folding or removable roof (hood), the latest types having a clip-on GRP roof, and the Torpedo or Spyder as a sports car with a fold-flat windscreen.

Design considerations

The management of a motor manufacturer entrusts the design office with the task of studying a new model of pre-determined size and class. The type of engine, piston displacement, basic construction characteristics (front- or rear-wheel drive, water- or air-cooled engine, two or four doors, etc.) and above all, the approximate price at which the car is to be marketed, are all outlined. Within the limits of these specifications, the chief designer fixes the external dimensions and wheelbase. This is determined by the space desired for the passengers; in fact the general layout of the car (see Figure 7) derives from the size of the passenger compartment. The passenger who wishes to travel in comfort, with legs outstretched and even wearing his hat, is not interested in the effect of the power unit's bulk on the overall space.

Besides passenger space, the designer must

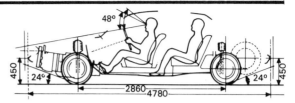

Figure 7 *Typical passenger car layout*

consider numerous other factors: the dimensions of the power unit and thus the capacity of the luggage compartment, the position of the spare wheel (should be easily available even with a full boot), bulk of the petrol tank, etc., and regulations regarding the height of headlamps, rear lights and bumpers must not be forgotten.

A pleasing body shape has to be set out to cut through the air without creating turbulence, slipping through and overcoming resistance with the minimum effort. Air spoilers may have to be integrated to deflect the airstream, lessen turbulence and provide greater adhesion for transmitting power to the driving wheels.

Computers are now used for analysing the road behaviour of cars. The computor is also used for calculating the dimensions of the structure and of the external surfaces. Having defined the line of the car a full-size plaster and wood model is scanned point by point over the whole of its surface by an electronic sensor which then feeds the special data to the computer. The computer integrates these stored measurements and gives continuous lines and geometrically perfect surfaces which are then reproduced on tapes used by the numerically controlled milling machines that prepare the high-precision dies. These dies are then used to produce the pressed metal panels.

At the same time, using a mathematical design model known as a finished element model, the surfaces and structural components of the car body are divided into the component geometrical units and subjected to examination by a computer to check their resistance to forces and deformation. In this manner, the maximum and most uniform utilization of the structures is obtained with minimum wastage of material without any additional weight, which would affect the fuel consumption, and in particular, avoiding non-uniform stresses which are dangerous to the safety and structural strength of the car. A properly balanced body, exactly dimensioned as a function of stress, is a guarantee also against corrosion.

Care should also be taken at the design stage to avoid all gaps and cavities, both in their actual shape and in the method of connection of the various parts because these could harbour dust and water. Hollow or box-type parts have to be designed so as to guarantee complete accessibility to paint, and to ensure their drainage and ventilation. The combination of different metals which could create unacceptable reactions has to be prevented by various insulation methods such as galvanizing, cadmium plating, plastic cladding and neutralizing.

Aerodynamics

The study of aerodynamics is essential in the design of cars but at the same time it imposes requirements that may be unacceptable in production models. The resistive force opposing the motion of a car through the air is termed aerodynamic drag and the work done in overcoming the force is dissipated as energy lost to the air flow. The amount of drag depends on the vehicle shape and varies with the square of the velocity of the vehicle relative to the air. Actual drag is the product of drag coefficient and frontal area.

A low-drag body (see Figure 8) will allow the car to reach higher speeds for a given power output. Conversely, reducing the power consumption at any particular speed, it leaves more power available for acceleration. Reducing the power requirement for a given performance can improve fuel consumption and so reduce the amount of fuel that needs to be carried. This, in turn, lessens the car's laden weight and further improves acceleration. Only in the matter of braking does the low-drag body impair performance since it offers less resistance to continued motion.

At speeds above 70 km/h (43.5 mile/h), aerodynamic drag exceeds 50% of the total resistance to motion and above 100 km/h (62 mile/h) it is the most important factor. The car's engine in its efforts to propel the vehicle has to overcome resistance of various kinds. In addition to the resistance of the tyres and mechanical components which absorb about 10% of the total power available, aerodynamic resistance is a major factor. Over the last ten years or so car manufacturers have become increasingly concerned with reducing air drag in their models. Aerodynamics, once the exclusive province of the aviation industry, is now a major consideration in car design. In the beginning, the aim was simply to achieve higher top speeds without necessarily increasing the engine power, but more recently, due to rapidly rising oil prices, the emphasis has moved to fuel economy. The more slippery a car, in terms of aerodynamic profile, the less power and hence less fuel is required to drive it along. The profile of the car is the main component of aerodynamic drag and is governed by the way in which the vehicle disturbs the air stream. Its behaviour was found not to accord with established aerodynamic theory evolved in aviation since the car had to maintain contact with the ground. Profile drag accounts for as much as 57% of the total aerodynamic drag for a typical saloon car.

Drag can also operate on a vehicle through skin friction and is dependent on the area and texture of the body licked by the air stream and responsible for 10 to 15% of aerodynamic drag. Skin friction is at its worst when air forced between the vehicle and the road increases in pressure and interferes with the vehicle underbody to create lift and pitching. This high-pressure air stream then spills out sideways around the lower body, mixes with the air streams on the body sides and forms a series of vortices (whirlpools). These, in turn, create induced drag which can account for as much as 10% of the total air drag. Both lift and

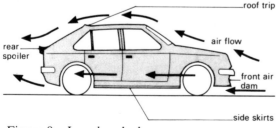

Figure 8   *Low-drag body*

pitch have undesirable effects, tending to reduce the pressure between the wheels and the ground, thus causing loss of traction on the rear axle and loss of steering on the front axle. A cleverly designed air dam at the front of the vehicle reduces the ground clearance and limits the volume of air passing under the body, thus reducing the pressure of the air stream under the car body. Low side skirtings then 'fence in' the air stream and prevent it from spilling out into the body side air streams. This greatly reduces the vortices and induced air drag.

In addition, the 'fencing-in' of the air traps a layer of air beneath the vehicle which acts as a smooth aerodynamic skin and reduces surface drag on the underbody. Above ground, roof-mounted trips and spoilers help to shape the air stream down over the back of the vehicle to reduce the vortices and cut down the car's wake.

Another air drag consideration is the resistance to air flow through the interior of the vehicle, notably of air taken in through the frontal apertures, passed through the radiator or heat exchanger and then usually left to go buffeting around in the engine compartment before finding its own way out. This cooling system resistance can account for about 10% of total air drag. Other items fitted to car bodies such as projecting door handles, mirrors, aerials, ornaments and decorative mouldings also interfere with the air flow and can account for as much as 15% of total aerodynamic drag.

Side force is formed by an asymmetric flow of air around the body and this force, acting at the

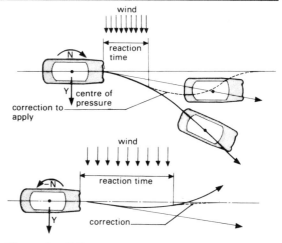

Figure 9 *Effects of side winds*

centre of pressure, can create moments about the centre of gravity. These moments are the cause of rolling and yawing, which may have a sizeable effect on the weight distribution on the wheels.

The serious effects of side winds are illustrated in Figure 9. If the centre of wind pressure is in front of the centre of gravity, the car will try to turn round like a wind-vane. Even allowing for a rapid reaction time, a considerable correction must be applied. When the centre of gravity lies in front of the centre of pressure, however, the car will tend to right itself.

As well as fuel economy, careful aerodynamic design results in straight-line stability, improved braking at high speed, considerable reduction in spray and dirt deposits in bad weather and the vehicle is easier to drive and safer.

3 Car body construction and finishing

Material requirements and body parts

The main requirements of the steel sheet used for making car bodies are as follows:

1 Low tensile strength and high ductility for ease of forming.
2 Easily assembled to form a body unit.
3 Light in weight.
4 Cheap as possible.

Low-carbon steel has these properties and is produced in large quantities for this purpose. A typical composition is:

Carbon	0.080%
Silicon	0.002%
Sulphur	0.020%
Phosphorus	0.020%
Manganese	0.350%

The liquid steel is cast into large ingots for subsequent hot-rolling to sheet. Typical sheet thicknesses in general use are:

10g	3.25 mm	Used for brackets and supports and heavy internal construction.
12g	2.65 mm	
14g	2.03 mm	Used in the panel assemblies which take the stress and load, (floor, bulkhead, sills, subframes, cross-members and inner stress panels).
16g	1.63 mm	
18g	1.22 mm	
20g	0.915 mm	Used for the outer panel construction (skin panels, doors, bonnet, boot lid, roof, wing panels).
22g	0.711 mm	

There has been strong competition between steel and aluminium for automotive applications and even though aluminium performs certain functions better than steel, the record of its displacement of steel includes very few pressings applications. The initial inroads made by aluminium were in castings for housings and engine blocks, both of which resulted in substantial savings in weight and cost. More recently, government requirements for improved fuel utilization in motor vehicles demand weight reductions of a magnitude that make aluminium's lower weight attractive despite its higher cost.

The most compelling demand for change in material properties has been the need for reduced weight and to meet this need a generation of improved high-strength steels has been developed that offers sufficient ductility to meet the fabrication requirements of the mass-production car industry. The new family of steels meet the minimum yield strength requirements and do so with improved ductility and weldability over steels previously available.

The differences between steel and aluminium that are responsible for the materials being competitive can be compared by giving steel a base of 1, so for the comparison of *tensile strength*, steel 1, aluminium $\frac{1}{3}$; *ductility*, steel 1, aluminium $\frac{1}{2}$; *density*, steel 1, aluminium $\frac{1}{3}$; *elastic modulus*, steel 1, aluminium $\frac{1}{3}$; and *cost per unit weight*, steel 1, aluminium 3. Thus for a tensile-strength-limited application, the replacement of steel by aluminium requires a cross-section that is three times greater, which makes it approximately equal in weight and modulus to steel but three times the cost. The factors that influence the material selection for car body pressings include yield strength, ductility, fatigue strength, formability, indentation resistance, fabricability and painting systems. New aluminium alloys can be heat-treated to the higher strengths associated with steels and this reduces the thickness for aluminium to about that of steel, but there is still a material cost penalty plus a per part heat-treatment cost. Also, heat-treatment experience on many motor vehicle parts has indicated excessive distortion.

Most automotive components are not loaded in pure tension, but where simple tensile properties are the design criteria, a steel with higher yield strength is capable of saving about 40% of the weight in a part. This is approximately comparable to any weight savings realised via aluminium substitution and is probably a cost saving also.

Functional requirements vary from simple bending or indentation resistance to complex twisting and structural loading of components. By changing to a higher-strength steel, appreciable weight reductions can be obtained. The type of improvement generally achieved by increasing the product strength can be as high as 30% and over.

Steel's mechanical properties have another inherent advantage over aluminium in their ability to absorb energy during deformation, thereby specifically providing improved energy absorption on impact loading.

Steel has historically proven its ability to be handled and fabricated into car body parts via pressings that can be easily welded into final components. The higher strength levels of the new steels have been successfully fabricated into complex parts with minimum die modifications. Adaptation of new dies to accept aluminium are similar to the changes that are required to accommodate the higher strength steels. To compensate for aluminium's lower modulus of elasticity, many aluminium parts require increased thickness. Thickness for thickness, aluminium substitution for steel requires larger spot-welding electrode diameters and greater edge distances. An aluminium thickness of 1.4 times that of steel is required to achieve an equivalent weld-bond strength when spot-welding light-gauge material. The disparity increases as thickness is increased with steel showing as much as a three-to-one strength advantage at a thickness of 2.2 mm.

Historically, the motor industry has used a.c. spot-welding equipment very successfully with steel, despite minor variations in energy output requirements. However, aluminium has an oxide coating that can vary significantly to an extent that it causes the production of unacceptable welds. The net effect of this is to require three-phase d.c. welding equipment which is costlier, bulkier and creates problems in high-volume, automated mass-production lines. In order to improve the inherent lack of spot weldability of aluminium sheet components, adhesive bonding and welding may have to be used to achieve satisfactory strengths. In production practice this introduces a high-cost construction procedure. Some complex aluminium parts need hot-forming to achieve the required deformation without failure and this again is a costly operation.

The ease of handling steel in a press shop with existing expertize, availability and lack of need for special processing, lubrication and die design means considerable cost savings in the manufacture of the vast majority of car body pressings. The use of aluminium brings with it an added cost penalty in as much as the paint system needed for it is not necessarily compatible with paints used for steel. Thus costs of a new paint line or special cleaning are incurred for switching over to the use of aluminium.

In summary, steel has many inherent advantages over aluminium for applications in automotive pressings. These consist of lower part cost, lower fabrication cost, utilization of existing fabrication techniques, welding, pressing and painting with significant cost savings. If new tooling design is required for changing to aluminium, then the new higher strength ductile steels remain competitive.

Identification and function of body pressings (see Figures 10 and 11)

The separate body and chassis construction in which the chassis resisted the bending and twisting

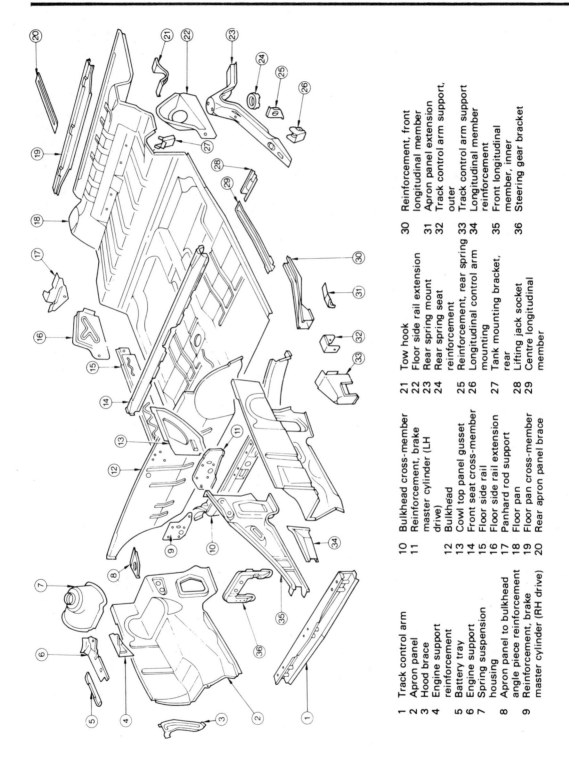

1   Track control arm
2   Apron panel
3   Hood brace
4   Engine support
    reinforcement
5   Battery tray
6   Engine support
7   Spring suspension
    housing
8   Apron panel to bulkhead
    angle piece reinforcement
9   Reinforcement, brake
    master cylinder (RH drive)

10 Bulkhead cross-member
11 Reinforcement, brake
    master cylinder (LH
    drive)
12 Bulkhead
13 Cowl top panel gusset
14 Front seat cross-member
15 Floor side rail
16 Floor side rail extension
17 Panhard rod support
18 Floor pan
19 Floor pan cross-member
20 Rear apron panel brace

21 Tow hook
22 Floor side rail extension
23 Rear spring mount
24 Rear spring seat
    reinforcement
25 Reinforcement, rear spring
26 Longitudinal control arm
    mounting
27 Tank mounting bracket,
    rear
28 Lifting jack socket
29 Centre longitudinal
    member

30 Reinforcement, front
    longitudinal member
31 Apron panel extension
32 Track control arm support,
    outer
33 Track control arm support
34 Longitudinal member
    reinforcement
35 Front longitudinal
    member, inner
36 Steering gear bracket

Figure 10   *Underbody assembly*

loads so that the body was purely functional has been superseded by the integral or mono-construction system. In this construction, frame members become an integral part of the body. Box sectioning of the body sills, door pillars and roof reinforcements form a framed structure in which stresses are distributed to all parts of the body.

In the reinforced body shell, the problem of primary importance is to prevent buckling of the body panels. A flat plate offers little resistance to buckling but curved plates with a single radius or better still, with a double radius or crown, provide excellent resistance; they are also convenient for the construction of a streamlined car. For stress-carrying parts of the body shell, greater rigidity can be achieved by the use of 'top hat' section or channel and angles built into the general assembly.

Mass production of car bodies in steel consists of the manufacture of sub-assemblies, usually a floor-pan, two sides, roof and cross-members, coming together on the assembly line to be spot-welded to form a complete body shell.

The underbody assembly

This positions the engine, transmission, the drive-line, together with the wheel-arches and seat positions. Strength is built into the floor by the transmission tunnel, which acts like an inverted channel section. The body sills or rocker panels provide longitudinal edge reinforcement. Laterally the floor pan is strengthened by box members at right angles to the transmission tunnel, generally in the areas of the front of the front seats and the front of the rear seats. The remaining area of 'flat' metal is ribbed or dished below the seats and in the foot wells to add stiffness to the sub-assembly. See Figure 10.

Body side assembly

The side frames reinforcing the floor pan will also transmit the loads between them. The front hinge pillar extends forward to meet with the dash panel and front bulkhead to provide great strength by 'boxing' the front end. The centre pillars are welded in between the body sill and the roof (or cant) rail. These are usually assembled as a box section using a 'top-hat' section and flat plate, with the flanges forming the attachment for the door weather seals. See Figure 11.

Shroud and dash panel assembly

The shroud and dash assembly is a complex structure connecting the two body sides across the car. It carries part of the forces set up by the front suspension and provides support for some of the weight of the power unit. The heater and its distribution chamber, the instruments and the steering column are all attached to this front cross-bracing. This assembly forms the front bulkhead of the body and is usually formed by assembling together several smaller panels (dash and shroud panels) which are joined by welds to form an integral unit. In some cases the windscreen frame is integral with the dash panel or cowl, which may extend upwards around the entire windscreen opening so that the upper edge of the cowl panel forms the front edge of the roof panel. In this case, the windscreen pillars, i.e. the narrow sloping construction at either side of the windscreen opening, are part of the cowl panel. In other constructions, only a portion of the windscreen pillar is formed as part of the cowl. See Figure 11.

This complete assembly is sometimes called the firewall because it is the partition between the passenger and engine compartment and openings in the cowl accommodate the necessary controls, wiring and tubing that extend from one compartment to the other. The instrument panel, which is usually considered as part of the cowl panel (although it is a complex panel itself), provides a mounting for the instruments necessary to check the performance of the vehicle during operation. On many passenger cars the front door hinge pillar is also an integral part of the cowl.

Roof and back window aperture panels

The roof panel is one of the largest of all major body panels and it is also one of the simplest in construction. Usually the roof is of all-steel, one-piece construction. The area of the roof cover

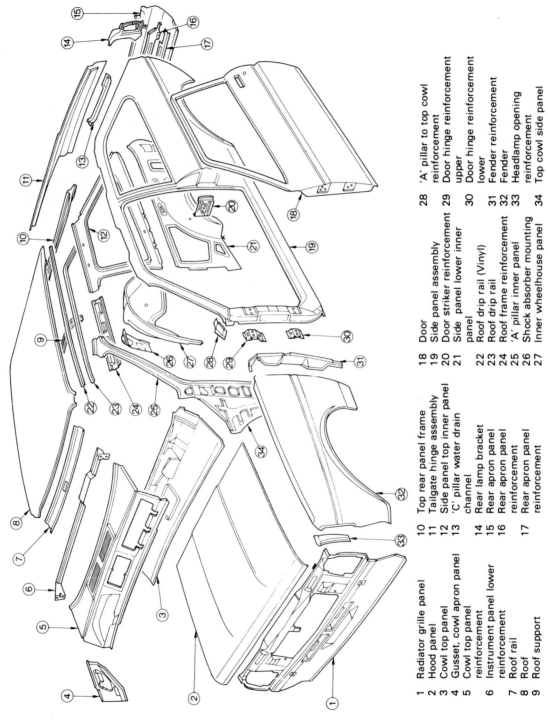

Figure 11   *Body assembly*

1   Radiator grille panel
2   Hood panel
3   Cowl top panel
4   Gusset, cowl apron panel
5   Cowl top panel reinforcement
6   Instrument panel lower reinforcement
7   Roof rail
8   Roof
9   Roof support

10   Top rear panel frame
11   Tailgate hinge assembly
12   Side panel top inner panel
13   'C' pillar water drain channel
14   Rear lamp bracket
15   Rear apron panel
16   Rear apron panel reinforcement
17   Rear apron panel reinforcement

18   Door
19   Side panel assembly
20   Door striker reinforcement
21   Side panel lower inner panel
22   Roof drip rail (Vinyl)
23   Roof drip rail
24   Roof frame reinforcement
25   'A' pillar inner panel
26   Shock absorber mounting
27   Inner wheelhouse panel

28   'A' pillar to top cowl reinforcement
29   Door hinge reinforcement upper
30   Door hinge reinforcement lower
31   Fender reinforcement
32   Fender
33   Headlamp opening reinforcement
34   Top cowl side panel

varies between different makes and models of cars. On some cars the roof panel ends at the front at the windscreen, whilst on others it extends downwards around the windscreen. On some cars the roof ends above the rear window at the rear while on others it extends downwards so that the rear window opening is in the lower rear roof. When the latter occurs, the roof forms the top panel around the rear boot opening.

The roof and its reinforcing members form the lid of the box structure. The stiffness of the roof is built in by the curvature given to it by the forming press whilst the reinforcement serves to stiffen the front and rear edges, building into the windscreen and rear window frames. Some roof panels have stiffeners consisting of small metal strips placed crosswise to the roof at intervals along the inside surface. These stiffeners are welded in place and provide tacking strips for securing the headlining and inside trim in place.

The centre pillar ('B–C' post) (Figure 12)

The centre pillar (termed 'B–C' post) acts as the central roof and side support between the front and rear of the car body side structure. For this reason its construction must be exceptionally strong, since it is the shut (lock) pillar for the front door and the hinge pillar for the rear door. In some car models the 'B–C' post is a wide fabrication with an outer panel surface, visible from the outside when the door is closed. The most common arrangement with two-door cars is for the 'B–C' post to act as the shut pillar for the doors. The centre pillar is irregular in shape since it must conform to the outside contours of the doors. Depressions are formed into the pillar to accommodate the door lock, striker plates and hinges, depending on the body style.

Rear bulkhead and parcel shelf

The rear bulkhead and the rear parcel shelf provide transverse stiffness, being welded between the body side frames and rear seat frame. In construction they are often pierced and flanged to increase rigidity.

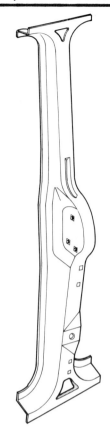

Figure 12
Typical
'B-C' post

The rear panel is curved to form part of the external shape of the body with its upper edge providing a support for the boot lid seal.

Front end work

The front end carries the engine and front suspension, steering gear and radiator. The suspension system, e.g. double wishbone or Macpherson strut, will affect detail design of the panels but, whatever system is used, the loads must be transmitted to the wings and/or wheel-arches and on into the body panels. The front cross-member assembly braces the front of the car and carries the radiator and headlamps. The side assemblies and front wheelhouse panel assembly form a housing for the wheel, a mating edge for the bonnet and a strong box section for attachment to the side frames and front bulkhead. See Figures 10 and 11.

Front wings

The front wings are each attached to the inner construction of the car body by means of a flange the length of the wing, which is turned inwards from the outside surface and through which securing bolts can pass. To add greater strength and to prevent vibration of supported edges, wing brackets are sometimes fitted. Adjustment for the front wing is usually provided for by slotting the boltholes. In some models the head and side lights are recessed into the front wing and fastened in place by flanges and reinforcement rims on the wing. The unsupported edges are swaged and turned inwards to give strength and prevent cracks developing in the edges of the wing due to vibration. This provides a smooth finished appearance to the edges of the wing.

Apart from covering the suspension construction and the wheel, the wing prevents water and mud from being thrown up onto the body by the wheels. In some cases flaps are necessary.

Front door panel assembly (Figure 13)

Several types of doors are used on each type of vehicle built, although the construction of the various doors is similar regardless of the location of the door on the vehicle. The door is composed of two main panels, an outer and an inner panel, both being of all-steel construction. The door derives most of its strength from the inner panel, since this is constructed mainly to act as a frame for the door. The outer panel flanges over the inner panel around the edges to form a single unit. The window channel may be welded or bolted to the inner door panel to provide support and direction to the window glass when it is raised or lowered.

The inner panel has holes or apertures drilled, punched or formed for attachment of the door trim. This trim consists of the window regulator assembly and the door locking mechanism. These assemblies are installed through the large apertures, usually in the middle of the inner panel.

Much of the thickness of the door is due to the depth of the inner panel which is necessary to

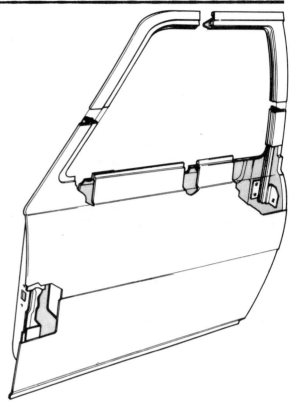

Figure 13   *Front door panel assembly*

accommodate the door catch and window mechanism. The inner panel forms the lock pillar and also the hinge pillar sections of the door. Small reinforcement angles are usually used between the outer and inner panels, both where the lock is inserted through the door and where the hinges are attached to the door. The outer panel is provided with an opening through which the outside door handle protrudes.

Bonnet panel assembly (Figure 14)

The bonnet is the panel covering the engine compartment; several types are in use on different makes of cars. Early models used a jointed type of bonnet held in place by bolts through the centre of the top of the bonnet into the body of the cowl and into the radiator panel. A piano-type hinge was used both where the bonnet hinged at the centre and at the sides. The most commonly used bonnet

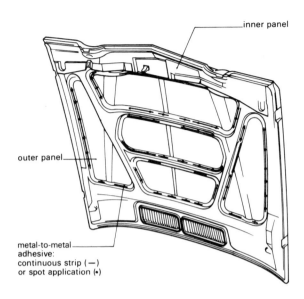

inner panel

outer panel

metal-to-metal
adhesive:
continuous strip (—)
or spot application (•)

Figure 14 *Bonnet panel assembly*

on later constructions is known as the mono or one-piece type and can be opened by a variety of different methods. On some models it is hinged at the front so that the rear end swings up when the bonnet is open. Others are designed to be opened from either side or unlatched at both sides and removed altogether. Most one-piece bonnets are of the alligator pattern, hinged at the rear so that the front end swings up when opened. Alligator bonnets have their catches at the front and in most cases are controlled from inside the car.

One-piece bonnets are quite large and, to make opening easier, the hinges are usually counter-balanced by means of tension or torsion springs. Where smaller bonnets are used, the hinges are not counterbalanced and the bonnet is held in place by a stay from the side of the wing or radiator panel to the bonnet.

The bonnet consists of the outer panel and inner reinforcement constructed in the 'H' or cruciform pattern. The reinforcement is basically a top-hat section to give rigidity to the component. A special type of epoxy resin is used to bond the structure under heat and pressure. This system avoids the dimpling effect on the outer surface that occurs in spot welding: preparation time for paintwork on

these components is considerably reduced. The main strength of the bonnet lies in the fact that the inner construction acts like a frame and the outer panel is formed round its edges, acting as flanges.

Boot lid assembly

The boot lid allows access to the luggage compartment and is composed of an inner and an outer panel. These panels are spot-welded together along their flanged edges to form a single unit. Some manufacturers use external hinges while others use concealed hinges attached to the inner panel only. A catch is provided at the bottom rear of the boot lid and is usually controlled by an external handle. The handle may be concealed from the eye under a moulding or some other type of trim. In some models, there is no handle on the rear boot lid, the hinges are spring loaded so that the lid rises automatically and is held in place by the hinge mechanism.

Body build, paint and sealing

From the press shop, the steel pressings pass into the body shop where the pieces of the jigsaw are welded together to form the strong rigid body shell. A car body is really made up of six major units – the floor, two sides, front end, rear end and the roof. These major sections are themselves made up from numerous smaller pressings and reach the main body-build conveyor as sub-assemblies from subsidiary 'feed' conveyers.

Special jig-base trucks, moving along a floor conveyor, carry the body floor assembly and pairs of heavy side-frame jigs holding the sides, front and rear sections mate up with the trucks so that all the units are clamped securely together while the welding is done.

The roof is the last major section to go on. Welding alone will not necessarily produce a watertight car body, so every joint is sealed with special compounds which do not set hard and which can stand great variations of temperature. At a later stage the bodies are given a very thorough watertightness test.

Various forms of welding are used in the building up of a car body shell – spot-welding, seam-welding, etc. Some of the huge multispot-welding machines in the body shop, working in pairs, make over 300 simultaneous spot-welds in a few seconds. In many body shops, there may be as many as 400 body shells passing through at one time on a conveyor system. After the body shells have collected their doors, bonnet panels and boot lids, they are prepared for the paint shop. Panel surfaces are inspected and blemishes in the sheet metal are removed with portable sanding machines.

Painting

There is more to painting car bodies than just giving them a coat of bright shiny colour. Painting means protection of the sheet metal, inside and out, underneath as well as on top.

The first stage in a long process is a multi-part rust-proofing treatment followed by almost complete immersion of the body shell in a huge bath of anti-rust alkyd primer. Next come two full coats of epoxy primer surfacer, including very-high-pressure application to the entire underbody, the wheel-arches and insides of the body sills. This primer is then baked in huge high-temperature ovens. After this the underbody area receives a thick coating of tough bituminous compound, which serves not only as an anti-corrosion protection for the sheet metal but also helps reduce road noise in the finished car.

The final stages complete the body protection process. The first stage is a base coat of acrylic paint with special adhesion qualities. This is followed by three coats of the finish colour paint, which is stored or 'baked' in a hot oven to create a really hard, deep-gloss finish. The acrylic paint has the virtue of keeping its shine for a long time without the need for frequent polishing by the owner. In between these operations there are a number of joint-sealing operations, rubbing-down stages, washings and cleanings. Another part of the car body protection operation involves spraying the insides of the body door sills with special anti-corrosion wax.

Sealing

The techniques of unitary body construction result in the unsealed body being vulnerable to corrosion and the entry of water, fumes and dust. The various locations on the vehicle body that require some form of seal against water/dirt ingress are

1   Areas where a permanently flexible seal is required, e.g. windscreen, rear screen.
2   External panel seams.
3   Areas where a seal is required to withstand stone pecking, e.g. wheel-arches, floor pan.
4   Protected areas where a bulk sealer is required.

It is essential for the various sealing materials (caulking compound, multi-purpose adhesive, metal joint sealer, windshield sealer, double-sided adhesive tape, PVC door foil, etc.) to be applied to clean dry surfaces if they are to adhere and form an effective seal. This condition can best be achieved by wiping the joint or seam with a solution of water and methylated spirit mixed in equal proportions and then blowing clean with a high-pressure jet of clean air.

Fixtures and fittings

From the paint shop, the body shells pass into the trim shop where they collect the scores of 'furnishing' items that turn them into car bodies. The bodies pass through a large number of 'stations' where the various items are fitted: carpets, seats, door handles, window glass, chrome mouldings, electric wiring, steering wheels, facia panels, etc. Many of the items fed to the main finish are made up in subsidiary assembly areas ranged along the trim shop – things like seats, door trim panels and instrument clusters.

Midway through this long 'furnishing' process when all the glass is in place, the body passes through a long water tunnel where it is drenched from every angle by powerful jets of water. This water contains a fluorescent dye and a special ultra-violet lamp is used to detect any drop of water that may have found its way into the body.

Before the trimmed bodies leave the trim-shop

floor, they collect some minor mechanical units like shock absorbers before being transferred to the 'body-drop' station where they descend to meet the main 'mechanicals' engines, gearboxes and axles delivered by conveyor from the machining areas. All the main 'feeder' conveyors delivering bodies, wheels and tyres, engines, gearboxes, etc., are synchronized, their speed being set to suit the daily output figure required. Finally, the car is driven off the end of the line under its own power to undergo a long series of checks and inspections before it leaves the building on the first stage of its journey to the customer.

Sound deadening

The sources of noise in cars

The noise inside a car comes from various sources. First, there is wind noise generated by the passage of air over the sharp external projections. This is an aerodynamic factor. Then there is mechanical airborne noise from the engine, gearbox and back axle. Most noises are complex mixtures of different frequencies; those at the lower end of the spectrum are termed 'boomy' or 'rumbly' and those at the higher end 'buzzy' or 'shrill'. Finally there is the noise generated by the sheet steel panels of the car body. These respond to the vibrations fed into the structure by the engine, gearbox, exhaust system, suspension and so on.

Noise reduction

Mechanical noise can be reduced by mounting the engine, gearbox and suspension on rubber insulators and by attaching the mechanical components themselves to strong points in the body structure. The cooling fan can be designed to minimize blade noise and the exhaust system hung to minimize its vibration range.

Body panels can be stiffened by swaging, the floor and bulkhead (areas which have the engine and suspension loads directly fed into them) being particularly important.

Where cost is not the overriding design factor, the engine and suspension can be rubber-mounted

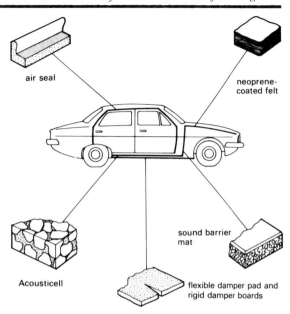

Figure 15　*Application of sound deadening materials*

on subframes which are in turn rubber-mounted to the body structure. Having eliminated many potential sources of noise by careful design, the job can be completed by sound insulation materials.

Since insulation costs money, many car manufacturers opt for the cheapest materials such as felt, which is not particularly efficient. The main requirements are to stop the mechanical noise getting into the passenger compartment, prevent the body panels generating noise and to absorb any noise that despite these precautions still gets through. The locations of the various sound-deadening materials are shown in Figure 15. The materials used can be described as follows:

Acousticell　A pressure-bonded blend of foam and textile fabric. This material combines the best features of synthetic and natural materials, soaks up noise and prevents reverberation. However, unlike felt, it does not 'mat down' in use and will not rot and give unpleasant smells if it gets damp.

Flexible damper pad and rigid damper boards These are self-adhesive and press into place. They stiffen up body panels, remove 'tinny' sounds and stop panel vibration and drumming. Damper boards are sometimes used double thickness for extra strength.

Sound barrier mat   This forms a positive barrier between noisy mechanical components and the passenger compartment. It consists of a flexible sound-proof layer bonded to thick foam and gives a far superior performance to felt. It is unaffected by oil fumes and engine compartment temperatures. The mat can be used in conjunction with non-hardening sealing mastic (so that it cannot crack and fall out) to permanently cure noise leaks round cables, hoses, etc.

Neoprene-coated felt   This is used on the bonnet to absorb noise and kill vibrations. The neoprene coating resists oil fumes.

Air seal   This is a self-adhesive closed-cell foam that cuts out wind noise and water leaks around door seals and quarter lights.

Corrosion in motor car bodies

Types of corrosion

Since general corrosion proceeds at roughly the same speed over the entire area exposed to a corrosive medium, it results in fairly even corrosion. Localized attack, the other type of corrosion, proceeds very rapidly in limited portions of the area, often taking the form of concentrated attacks, resulting rather quickly in holes or cracks. The commonest types of localized attack in cars are

1   *Crevice corrosion*, which occurs in narrow gaps filled with liquid. It is usually caused by so-called 'differential aeration cells'. A cell forms because the oxygen in the air has greater difficulty penetrating the gap than it does the rest of the surface. As a result, the steel inside the gap becomes an anode and corrodes while the steel at the aperture of the gap becomes a cathode protected against corrosion. Crevice corrosion is often aggravated by moisture remaining longer in the gap than in other areas because drying takes place more slowly.

2   *Deposit attack*, which can occur beneath non-metallic deposits and coatings. It is due to moisture being retained by the deposit so that a differential aeration cell develops in the same way as in the crevice corrosion.

3   *Corrosion fatigue*, which is damage inflicted on the material as a result of varying loads, combined with the influence of a corrosive medium. It can result in cracks.

4   *Pitting*, which covers small areas, but can often attain considerable depths.

5   *Galvanic corrosion*, which occurs when two different materials are combined to form a galvanic cell. Usually the materials are two different metals such as steel and copper or aluminium.

General corrosion

General corrosion mainly occurs in vehicles in large areas of uncoated steel, often in wheel-arches, where gravel thrown up by the wheels has worn away the protective surface coating of paint and underbody compound. This type of corrosion also occurs in underbody members and pillars that are penetrated by dampness. If spaces of this kind are also filled with dirt from the road, the corrosion will often be combined with deposit attack. Atmospheric conditions commonly influence the speed with which general corrosion occurs, depending on the following:

a   How long the surface stays wet.
b   Relative humidity of the air.
c   Air temperature.
d   Level of air pollution, especially of sulphur dioxide and chloride content.

The most important of these is the length of time the surface is wet, for example, from rain or damp snow. Thus, the speed of corrosion on a dry surface outdoors, even at 90% humidity, is less than 1% of that on a surface dampened by rain.

The underbody member surfaces, filled with road dirt and water, remain damp for very long periods, even after other parts of the car are dry. Floor sections inside the car often rust because they are subjected to prolonged dampness. The water that succeeds in penetrating these sections (for example, through leaking windows and doors or brought in as snow) often collects under the rubber mat covering the floor. Such moisture can be retained for a long time, especially if there is felt or foam rubber insulation underneath the rubber.

There is still more risk of rapid corrosion if the floor sections are constructed so that there are cavities or other spaces where water can collect. Similar damage also occurs in doors. Clogging of the drainage holes at the bottom of doors can allow considerable water to be entrapped there, causing the door to rust through, usually at the bottom.

On a surface covered with road dirt containing salt, for example, corrosion can proceed at a lower relative humidity than on a clean surface. Temperature has relatively little effect on the speed of atmospheric corrosion, but in some cases an increased temperature may help to speed up the corrosion of certain underbody components. In some vehicle models corrosion is far more frequent on underbody members that are near the exhaust system. If such a member is filled with dirt and moisture, the higher temperature causes faster corrosion before the moisture evaporates, which, however, is often impeded by component design. On exposed surfaces and in well ventilated spaces, by contrast, a rise in temperature will cause the surface to dry rapidly, thus reducing the speed of corrosion. Sometimes local rises in temperature can cause snow and ice to melt, with corrosion proceeding even during very cold periods, when other underbody components are negligibly affected.

The presence of air pollutants, especially sulphur dioxide and chlorides, affects the speed of atmospheric corrosion and the latter entails a risk of galvanic corrosion, crevice corrosion and pitting. Chlorides also help to speed up the disintegration of painted surfaces.

Corrosion is also promoted by acid from batteries. If a battery is located in a badly ventilated space, such as under the rear seat, the acid gives rise to corrosion in the rear floor section or in adjacent underbody members.

Crevice corrosion and deposit attack

Crevice corrosion can occur when constricted gaps are filled with water. When sheet metal components are welded together or onto members, brackets, etc., narrow gaps are almost invariably formed between the sheets. Side members in some cars are made up of a number of profiled sheets joined together by spot-welding and if the gaps are not filled with some form of coating or sealing compound, rust will often develop eventually causing the joints to disintegrate. Sometimes corrosion can be aggravated by the gap between two components being filled with a porous liner which can retain moisture. Another type of 'gap' often occurring in cars consists of narrow spaces between underbody members and wings, around bowl-shaped reinforcements in 'U'-shaped upward-turned profiles, or in the angles between two members. All of these spaces are easily filled with road dirt which can give rise to crevice corrosion and deposit attack.

Corrosion fatigue

Corrosion fatigue occurs in certain car models near spring mountings. This weakens the structure and, combined with shock and vibration, eventually results in cracks.

Pitting

Pitting can occur when paintwork is damaged, perhaps by loose stones. The exposed metal surface of the area where rust damage occurs beneath the paintwork form an anode and corrosion occurs which can eventually cause a body plate to rust through. In the worst cases the whole process takes only a few months.

Pitting also frequently occurs in decorative chrome-nickel coatings on components such as bumpers, door handles and mouldings. In coatings of the older type, consisting of a layer of nickel with a layer of chrome superimposed, the attack will penetrate as far as the base material, giving rise to rust patches. Newer kinds, known as double nickel coatings, consist of a semi-bright inner nickel layer and an outer layer of bright nickel which in turn is covered by one or two layers of chrome. Pits in such coatings do not as a rule penetrate beyond the semi-bright nickel layer, at which point they spread out sideways. This form of corrosion, which is known as intermediate layer corrosion, spoils the appearance of the surface finish.

Vehicle exhaust fumes can also have a corrosive effect, which is sometimes manifested through aggravated corrosion of the bumper near the exhaust pipe. Road dirt is an accelerating factor, especially if is contains salt.

Anodized aluminium, which is used on the decorative parts of some cars, is also subject to

pitting, which can penetrate the thin oxide layer of the metal surface and give rise to grey corrosion crusts, which are darkened by dirt.

Galvanic corrosion

Galvanic corrosion is a type of electrochemical reaction due to the effect of a galvanic cell in which the electrodes generally consist of different metals. The predominant construction material in cars is steel and galvanic corrosion can occur when this is combined with more or less noble metals. When steel is combined with more noble metals, such as copper or brass, galvanic corrosion occurs in the steel. When steel is joined with a less noble

Table 1 *Types and commonest causes of corrosion in various car components*

Components	Materials	Types of corrosion	Causes
Chassis members, pillars	Sheet steel	Crevice corrosion, general corrosion, deposit attack	Moisture and road dirt entering members, gaps, welds, etc.; damage to paintwork from flying stones; gravel wearing away protective surface coating.
Spring and other force-transmitting mountings	Sheet steel	Crevice corrosion, general corrosion, corrosion fatigue	Moisture and road dirt filling gaps and pockets formed by reinforcements around the mountings
Floor sections	Sheet steel	General corrosion, crevice corrosion, deposit attack	Moisture collecting under carpets and in gaps especially along edges
Wings	Sheet steel	Pitting, general corrosion, crevice corrosion, deposit attack	Damage to paintwork from flying stones; gaps and shelves where road dirt traps moisture; gravel wearing away protective surface coating
Doors	Sheet steel	General corrosion, crevice corrosion, deposit attack	Water collecting in inadequately drained door construction
Brake lines	Zinc-coated steel tubing	Galvanic corrosion, pitting	Zinc coating corrodes, exposing layer of copper; galvanic corrosion occurs where there are pores in the copper
Bumpers	Steel with decorative chrome–nickel coatings; anodized aluminium	Pitting	Road dirt and exhaust fumes accelerating corrosion process

metal, the latter corrodes as in the case of light metal alloy wheel rims fitted with steel rivets and also with corrosion in aluminium body panels on steel framework. In the latter case corrosion is accelerated by road salt.

For ease of reference the types and commonest causes of corrosion in various car components are tabulated in Table 1.

Basic body repair principles

The first essential step in the rectification of accident-damaged car bodies is to make a thorough and complete assessment of the damage involved. If the damage is other than minor in nature, then in addition to direct visible damage caused by the impact, consequential or indirect damage can well exist in areas some considerable distance from the point of impact, due to hidden distortion of structural components. It is a fundamental rule of accident repair work that the repair operations must be carried out in the reverse order of the forces and stresses causing the damage. The assessment therefore should determine the cause and extent and also the sequence in which the damage occurred. If during this assessment, damage or distortion which will affect body align-

ment is apparent or suspected, then it will be necessary to carry out a body alignment check using purpose-built jigs. From this the most economical method of repair for all damaged areas should be determined.

The repair options available to the body repairer are

1 Cutting out and replacing severely damaged panels and members.
2 Straightening and reshaping less severely damaged panels and members; alternatively, using part panels to replace damaged sections of body panels.

The panel, or part panel, replacement method of repair is often the most economical due to the availability and low cost of replacement parts compared with the high labour costs of panel beating and straightening seriously damaged parts.

In the event of damage to front or rear end of the vehicle involving suspension or steering components, it is essential that the replacement parts are replaced in correct alignment to the undamaged bodyshell. For the alignment to be correctly carried out it is essential that a body-alignment jig is used to set the panels prior to welding.

4 Commercial vehicle terminology

Articulated vehicle The combination of a tractor and semi-trailer unit.

Articulated trailer See 'Semi-trailer'.

Axle loading The maximum weight, laid down by chassis manufacturers, that individual axles can carry.

BBC Abbreviation for the distance from the bumper to the back of the cab.

Bearers The cross-members that support the body floor. They are located on either chassis members or longitudes.

Box van A vehicle body having a rigid shell.

Bulker A general term for liquid- and powder-carrying vehicles.

Bulkhead The front panel of a van body immediately behind the vehicle cab.

Bump height The distance from the top of the chassis to the underside of the floor/wheelbox, recommended by chassis manufacturer.

Cab The part of a vehicle enclosing the driver.

Cant rail The member which connects the side panels of vans to the roof structure.

Chassis The general description for a vehicle without a body. Abbreviation of the term 'chassis cab'.

Chassis van The combination of a van body and trailer chassis.

Chassisless van A specialist trailer van which has no chassis frame, all loads and imposed stresses being carried by the body structure. All running gear is fixed directly to the body structure.

Cleat Bracket used for joining longitudinals to transverse body members.

COE Abbreviation for 'cab over engine'.

CV Abbreviation for 'commercial vehicle'.

Demountable Vehicle bodies that can be lifted on and off chassis by vehicle-mounted mechanical or hydraulic equipment.

Dolly A set of wheels placed under the front of a semi-trailer to convert it into a drawbar trailer.

Double bottom Articulated vehicle with a drawbar trailer.

Drawbar trailer A trailer having wheels at front and rear.

Dropside panels Hinged panels which are fitted to the sides of platform bodies.

Dropwell Area of floor at the rear of a body, which has been lowered to facilitate loading.

Drumming See 'Panting'.

Dunnage Material used in stowing cargo within a vehicle to prevent movement.

Fifth wheel A coupling device mounted on a tractor unit and used to connect a semi-trailer to the tractor of an articulated vehicle.

Flatbed A vehicle body having only a floor and bulkhead. Sometimes called a platform.

Forward control Term to describe a cab built over the engine.

Glasonite Proprietary name for GRP/ply.

GRP Abbreviation of glass reinforced plastic, used for vehicle roofs and some vehicle cabs.

GRP/ply One-piece vehicle panels having a plywood core faced with GRP.

GVW Gross vehicle weight. The total weight of a complete vehicle with all ancillary equipment, fuel, oil and water, and with payload and driver.

GCW Gross combination weight. The gross vehicle weight as applicable to articulated tractor/ trailer combinations.

GTW Gross train weight. The gross vehicle weight as applicable to a vehicle and separate drawbar trailer combination.

HGV Abbreviation for 'heavy goods vehicle', i.e. all vehicles over 7.5 tonnes gross weight.

HGT or HGVT Abbreviation for 'heavy goods vehicle test'. Applicable to all vehicles over 7.5 tonnes gross weight.

Headboard The panel at the front of a platform vehicle body, immediately behind the cab.

Huckbolt Special rivet used in body-building.

'I' value A measurement of the geometric properties of a section used in structural calculation, primarily for deflection levels.

Kickplate The section that connects internally, on vans, between the vertical pillars and the floor and restrains loads from damaging side sheets.

Kerb weight Weight of complete vehicle and all equipment, but without payload or driver. This weight is commonly quoted by all chassis manufacturers, excluding the body weight.

King pin The coupling pin situated in the centre of the front underside of a semi-trailer chassis, which couples to the towing tractive unit via the fifth wheel.

Landing gear The support legs in the front part of a semi-trailer which can be cranked up or down and used to support the front of the trailer when the tractive unit is removed.

Longitudes The main longitudinal members of a body which normally rest upon the chassis.

Luton Box van with extension over vehicle cab.

Moment of inertia See 'I value'.

Normal control Term to describe normal bonnet-type cab, i.e. cab behind engine.

Overhang The dimensions from the centre-line of the rear axle to the rear of the body. Many chassis manufacturers quote a maximum recommended dimension.

Pantechnicon A van having an integral construction with a low floor height for ease of loading. Often referred to as a furniture removal van.

Panting A term used to describe the vibrations/rigidity of van side panels.

Payload The difference between gross vehicle weight and unladen weight.

Plated weight A statement of all relevant legislative weights applicable to a vehicle, given by the chassis manufacturer.

Platform See 'Flatbed'.

Platform skeletal A skeletal trailer which has a full floor in order to facilitate operation as a flatbed and container carrier.

PTO Abbreviation for 'power take off', which is a device fitted to gearboxes in order to transmit power to ancillary equipment.

Rail See 'Cant rail' and 'Rave'.

Rave Often referred to as the bottom rail, this is the longitudinal section which mates with the outer extremities of the floor and bearers and, in the case of vans, connects with the side panel.

Reefer A term used to describe insulated/refrigerated van bodies and containers.

Rigid This is a vehicle in which the body, chassis and cab are permanently connected and do not rotate relative to one another.

Rope hooks Fittings fixed to raves of open-top vehicles in order to secure tilts/tarpaulins.

Rub rail   A longitudinal section fitted to van sides in order to minimize damage to side sheets.

Running gear   A term used to describe axles, springs, wheels and other items fixed to the underside of a trailer chassis.

Section modulus (Z value)   The geometric properties of a section used in structural calculations primarily for determining stress levels.

Semi-trailer   A trailer having wheels at the rear and connected to the tractor by means of a king pin.

Skeletal   A flatbed vehicle or trailer with no floor designed to carry containers.

Shroud plate   Shaped sheet/plate below rear aperture designed to conceal underframe members. Often used to mount number plates or rear lights.

Shutter   Abbreviation used for roller shutter doors.

Spandrel   Panel above rear aperture designed to increase torsional rigidity of rear frame and to hide roller shutter door mechanism.

Split 'P'   A 'P'-shaped section used as an outer frame for dropside panels.

Stripping   Term to describe removing load from a vehicle.

Stuffing   Term to describe loading a vehicle.

Tailboard   A rear-opening panel hinged in the horizontal plane.

Tailift   A power-operated tailboard combined with lift mechanism to permit ground to floor level loading.

Tanker   A body having a round or elliptical cross-section, used for carrying liquids and powders.

Tarp   See 'Tilt'.

Tilt   Abbreviation used for tarpaulin/nylon load cover used on flats and TIR trailers – often used in conjunction with framework.

Tipper   A fixed-side vehicle that can be mechanically/hydraulically lifted at the front end, whilst pivoting at the rear end, in order to shed its load.

TIR   Abbreviation for 'Transports Internationales Routiers', a convention governing construction and use of vehicles operating under customs seal.

Truck   General term used to describe goods-carrying vehicles.

Tractor   The power unit of an articulated semi-trailer.

'U' bolt   A 'U'-shaped bracket for securing the body to the chassis.

ULV (unladen weight)   This is the kerb weight of a vehicle less an allowance for fuel, oil, water and tools. This is the weight used for taxation purposes.

Van   General term used to describe box, Luton and pantechnicon-type vehicles.

Wheelbase   For all rigids and articulated vehicles used prior to 1 June 1973, this is the distance from the centre-line of the front axle to the centre-line of the rear axle. For articulated vehicles not used prior to 1 June 1973, this is a combination of the axle spread of the tractor unit and the distance from rear axle to the leading trailer axle.

Wheelbox   Fabrication used on inside of vehicles to enclose wheels.

X bearers   Abbreviation for 'cross-bearers'.

Z value   See 'Section modulus'.

5 Commercial vehicle types

Panel vans (Figures 16 and 17)

These light commercial vehicles, up to 3.5 tonnes GVW, are very popular with tradesmen for door-to-door and high street deliveries. Many of the lighter models are based on the standard motor car underbody arrangement. The bodies are steel pressings with large doors to faciliate entry and exit and access for loading and unloading by one or two doors at the rear. Almost all are of unitary or integral construction.

Figure 16 *Light panel van based on motor car underbody arrangement*

Production van variations

The standard van arrangement (Figure 18) is used for general local delivery work and, after body shell conversions and interior fitting out, for ambulances, motor caravans and security vans.

The chassis cab arrangment shown in Figure 19 comes in three different versions: tippers and dropsides (A), box vans (B) and Luton head vans (C).

The chassis dash arrangement (Figure 20) is used extensively for integral body/cab 'walk-through' type vans.

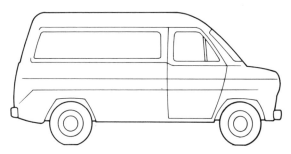

Figure 17 *Panel van*

Medium and heavy goods vehicles

Medium vehicles (Figure 21)

Medium four-wheeled rigids up to 7.5 tonnes GVW may be driven by a person holding a normal driving licence, making the vehicles very popular with operators in the distributive business.

The cab must be easy to enter and leave as many of these vehicles are used for house and shop

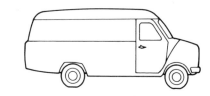

Figure 18 *Standard van*

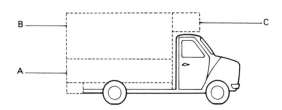

Figure 19 *Chassis cab*

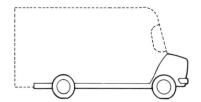

Figure 20   *Chassis dash*

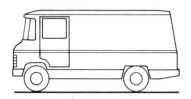

Figure 21   *Medium commercial vehicle walk-through van*

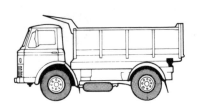

Figure 22   *Heavy haulage truck*

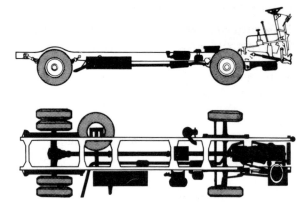

Figure 23   *Four-by-two rigid*

Figure 24   *Rigid vehicle with drawbar trailer*

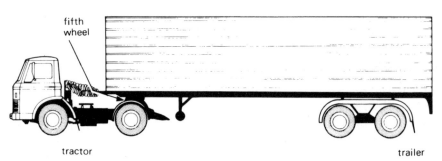

fifth wheel

tractor

trailer

Figure 25   *Articulated vehicle*

deliveries. Most of these vehicles are of separate body and chassis construction, a custom-built body on a standard chassis cab or chassis cowl.

Heavy goods vehicles (Figure 22)

These are the very robust vehicles weighing 7.5 tonnes or over (up to the maximum legal GVW), powered by a diesel engine and used for haulage work. The load carried generally requires twin tyres fitted side by side on the rear wheels. When the load is very heavy more axles are required.

Rigid vehicles (Figure 23)

These non-articulated vehicles are classified by the total number of wheels and the number of driving wheels, e.g. 4 × 2 indicates a four-wheeled vehicle having two driving wheels. Two separate road wheels secured to one hub are regarded as one wheel for this purpose.

Rigid vehicle with drawbar trailer (Figure 24)

A rigid vehicle may have two, three or four axles and can be adapted to pull a drawbar trailer. These vehicles are not so popular since the advent of articulated vehicles and demountables.

Articulated vehicles (Figure 25)

These haulage vehicles consist of a detachable trailer which is supported on a platform on the tractor unit; the connection is called a fifth wheel. Loads carried must not exceed the gross train weight (GTW).

There are applications in which a rigid vehicle is preferable to an articulated vehicle. An operator can benefit from the greater frame rigidity and strength of the rigid, particularly where off-the-road and site work is involved. Tippers on rigid chassis are less subject to strain fracture in the frame and body than some types of artic. For off-the-road work multi-axle rigid vehicles have the advantage that four-wheeled drive can be made available at the rear bogey which greatly improves traction.

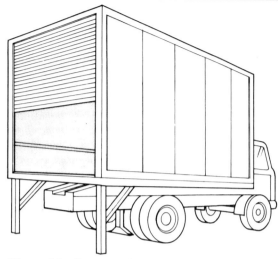

Figure 26 *Demountable body*

The initial cost of a rigid vehicle can be less because the body is mounted on the chassis without the need for a separate trailer frame, brake-system and fifth-wheel coupling. A rigid vehicle will not jack-knife, will not give trailer swing and is less likely to overturn.

Demountables (Figure 26)

Demountable rigid trucks, drawbar trailers and semi-trailers with built on, self-motivated body-exchanging facilities are probably the most important distribution-cost-reducing development in commercial road transport since articulated vehicles came on the scene. Like the articulated vehicle, the demountable leaves its cargo-carrying components behind for loading whilst the prime mover component (chassis cab) continues with other pre-loaded cargo units. Unlike the articulated which leaves behind sophisticated and expensive trailers, the demountable leaves only a simple and relatively low-cost body unit to stand on legs. Thus, a much higher proportion of the capital equipment achieves maximum utilization.

Cab types

The type of driver's cab mounted on a commercial vehicle chassis is, in the main, determined more by the function of the vehicle rather than by its size. Commercial vehicles operating in cities and in local traffic have their doors positioned behind the front axle to enable easier and quicker access to the cab. The difference in height between the road and the driver's seat should not be too great and adequate step arrangements in a favourable position should be provided.

The requirements for heavy, long-distance haulage truck cabs calls for a more luxurious layout of the working place of the driver. The easy entrance into the cab is not as important. Here the requirements are comfort, favourable shaping of the controls and ease of operation (power assistance) to give low fatigue levels, adequate insulation to keep noise levels down, all-steel construction to meet proposed EEC regulations, crash padding, well spaced demisters, a high vision point, large 12-kW heater and through-flow ventilation with extra air-in air-out vents at the door tops.

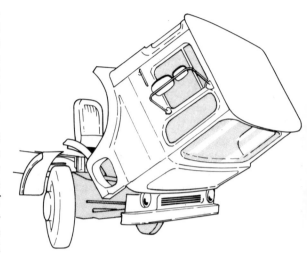

Figure 29   *Tilt cab*

Figure 27   *Normal control*

Figure 28   *Forward control*

Normal control (Figure 27)

A normal control vehicle is designed with the engine located forward of the cab to give more cab space, less noise and heat and ease of entry and exit.

Forward control (Figure 28)

This type has its cab built over the engine and has the advantage of additional length available for the payload and a better angle of vision. Its disadvantages include less cab space for the crew and engine maintenance can be more difficult unless specialized equipment is available or the cab is designed to tilt forward (see Figure 29).

A variation to forward control aimed at giving ease of entry and exit for door-to-door delivery work and more space for the crew is the semi-forward control type.

Functional types

The need for specilization in transport has created a demand for a whole group of commercial vehicle bodies which can be classified according to their functions. Vehicles such as platform types, dropsides, box vans, Luton head vans, pantechnicons, livestock carriers, hoppers, tankers, tippers, glass-carriers, refuse disposal trucks, mobile shops, fire engines, exhibition vehicles, and sleeper cabs (see Figure 30) are just a few of the many, each requiring its own special design and construction considerations.

Figure 30   *Sleeper cab*

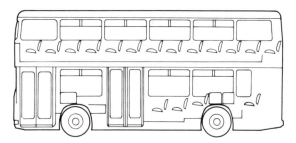

Figure 31   *Town bus*

Bus and coach types

Passenger-carrying vehicles are most easily classified according to the distance that the vehicle has to cover before having to stop for passengers. There are, therefore, differences between town buses, suburban buses, inter-city buses and touring coaches.

Town buses (Figure 31) are used for short journeys, having standing space, wide entrance and exit doors with entry and exit platforms and relatively hard seating usually covered with durable trim materials such as PVC or moquette or a combination of both.

Suburban buses (Figure 32), depending on area, operate at distances around 40 km, have reasonably comfortable seating and fairly small entry platforms. Usually one door is sufficient for this type of operation.

Inter-city buses operating up and down the motorways are competing with rail and air travel and have to attract passengers with more luxurious interiors, very comfortable seats, adequate luggage pens and roof-racks for hand luggage.

For the longer-distance touring coaches (Figure 33) often called luxury coaches, very comfortable reclining seats are installed with air-conditioning, radios and reading lights provided. Additional windows in the roof are used to improve visibility for the passengers and for cooling and fresh air. Thermal/acoustic insulation in these luxury

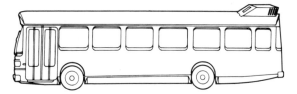

Figure 32   *Suburban bus*

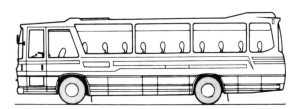

Figure 33   *Luxury touring coach*

coaches is very elaborate and adequate spacious luggage compartments are provided.

These vehicles can also be classified according to size and passenger-carrying capacity; the approximate passenger capacity is as follows:

Minibus	8–15
Small coaches for long distances	16–30
Small buses for towns	Up to 40
Medium-bodied coaches for long distance	31–45
Medium buses for towns	41–60
Large coaches for long-distance touring	46–60
Large buses for towns	61–80
Large town buses (recently)	80 plus

6 Methods of body construction

Types of body structure

The different types of body structure stem from the overall design concepts of a vehicle, but basically there are three main variations:

1 The non-load-carrying (orthodox), separate body and chassis type.
2 The semi-integral type.
3 The integral type.

In the separate body and chassis type of construction, the loads on the vehicle are transferred to the suspension entirely by a separate chassis. This type of construction was used in the early days of vehicle development, the chassis frame carrying all the loads and the bodywork either being made of flexible material (traditionally wood) or being made of stiff material (steel or aluminium alloy), but isolated from the chassis deflection by body mountings usually of rubber. This type of construction survives in both forms where wooden load-carrying bodies are rigidly attached to the chassis frame but the stiff metal cabs are mounted on flexible cab mounts. When the body mounts are replaced by relatively stiff material that prevents squeaking, due to the relative displacement between the body and chassis, some of the load is transferred to the body structure and it becomes semi-integral. The amount of load carried by the body structure is dependent on the number of attachments (mountings) to the chassis and on the mount stiffness.

Semi-integral construction makes use of side outriggers attached to the chassis longitudinal framing and onto which the body side structure is fixed, both chassis frame and body structure

sharing the loads imposed in service. Many passenger service vehicle bodies are constructed in this manner but such vehicles are heavy with a poor power-to-weight ratio and errors in body design can introduce large forces into the body structure which may not have been designed to receive them.

The faults of semi-integral methods of construction led to the introduction of fully integral body construction where part of the load previously carried by the chassis is now diffused through the body structure so that each part of the body shell structure is load-carrying, i.e. the body shell itself becomes a load-carrying beam. A smaller number of components is needed and the vehicle is both lighter and stronger.

Types of body construction

Due to local variations in design, the following can only serve as a general guide in identifying the various types of bodywork construction.

All-metal (pressed steel) This method is associated in the main with the manufacture of light commercial vehicle bodywork (panel vans, for example), employing high volume or mass production techniques. Extensive use is made of light-gauge steel pressings assembled by welding with the aid of jigs and fixtures. A range of standard commercial vehicle cabs is also produced in large numbers using these production methods and techniques.

Timber (Figure 34) Wood is normally used for commercial bodywork built in small numbers to

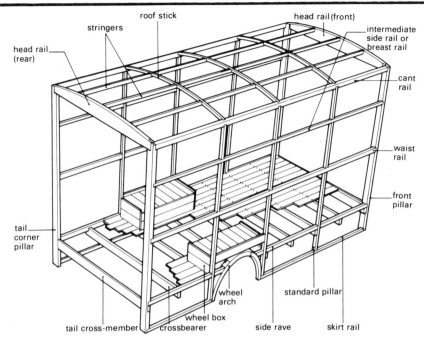

Figure 34 *Timber-framed box van*

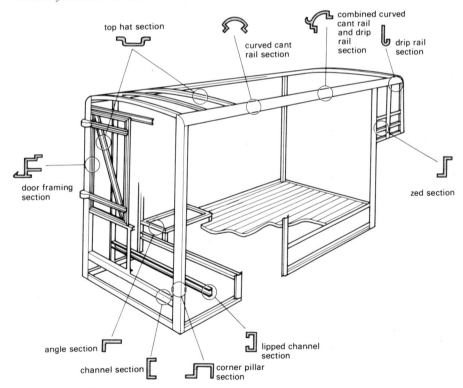

Figure 35 *Aluminium alloy body construction*

specific requirements. Panel cladding is normally in aluminium and/or reinforced plastics materials (plywood for certain specialized applications). In certain cases this type of arrangement may be referred to as timber-framed composite construction.

Aluminium This method makes extensive use of aluminium alloy extruded sections assembled by welding, bolting and/or riveting (see Figure 35). Cladding is usually in aluminium sheet material (GRP panels in certain cases).

Composite This type of construction involves vehicle bodies employing a variety of materials in their construction. There are several types including steel-framed bodywork employing extensive use of hot- and cold-rolled steel sections assembled by welding, bolting and/or riveting:

1 Steel structure of cold-rolled sections with timber packings onto which panel cladding and body hardware components are fixed (Figure 36).
2 Timber structure with flitch plates (steel plate) reinforcement on major structural members, e.g. crossbearers, pillars, waistrails, etc. (Figure 37).
3 Structures comprising various materials, e.g. timber cross-bearers, steel or aluminium side raves (Figure 38).

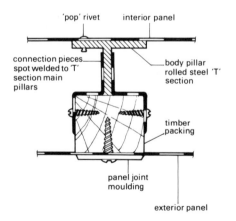

Figure 36 *Typical steel-framed bus body pillar section*

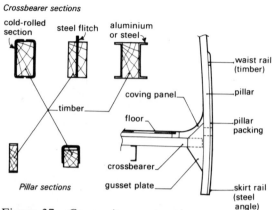

Figure 37 *Composite construction*

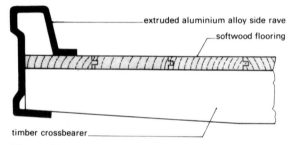

Figure 38 *Composite construction*

The interior and exterior panel cladding for composite construction is either steel, aluminium, reinforced plastics materials or plywood (in certain cases) and the flooring of metal, timber and/or plywood.

GRP (glass-reinforced plastics) This type of construction is used on refrigerated commercial vehicles; the body shell may be moulded in one piece or several major parts. The shell is suitably reinforced (as necessary) with timber and/or steel inserts and packings to add strength, aid assembly and attach body components, e.g. mirrors, handrails, hinges, etc.

Truck selection

Some of the factors that have to be considered by operators when selecting a vehicle for use with a known body and/or equipment are:

Type of load All the calculations carried out by chassis and body engineers assume that, within reasonable limits, the load to be placed in the body will be evenly distributed along and across the body. If the body or equipment to be mounted constitutes an unevenly distributed load, calculations should be made with regard to axle loads in laden, unladen and part-laden conditions.

Diminishing loads The mode of operation for which the vehicle is intended should be investigated. If a vehicle is near the axle load limit in the laden condition and a portion of the load is removed from the rear of the vehicle, while the rear axle load will decrease, the front axle load will increase possibly to above the load limit.

Body and payload weight The type of body, its weight and the payload capacity required must be determined. The vehicle wheelbase, and hence chassis length, should be chosen with due regard to the body length envisaged.

Type of operation If the vehicle is intended for use on only metalled roads, there are different design considerations with regard to the body and its mounting than if it is to be used 'off-road' for a part or all of the time.

Loading and discharge Installations such as crane hoists, tail lifts, roof-mounted hanging equipment, etc., all have a bearing on vehicle performance and should be considered. Bulk powder transport loading may well be from overhead whilst discharges may be through hoppers or suction equipment, separate or as an integral part of the bodywork. Some special-purpose bodies have to be provided with variations in the floor levels, elevating roofs, well floors, opening sides and bodywork so that it can be raised to other levels than the normal one on the chassis frame.

Hydraulic tail lifts (Figure 39)

Installing tail lifts increases vehicle utilization, brings economies and increases driver comfort and productivity. Heavy and bulky loads, on wheeled pallets or individually carried, can be loaded and unloaded by one person quickly and easily.

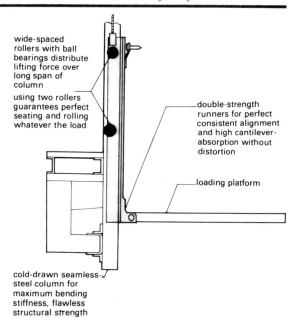

wide-spaced rollers with ball bearings distribute lifting force over long span of column

using two rollers guarantees perfect seating and rolling whatever the load

double-strength runners for perfect consistent alignment and high cantilever-absorption without distortion

loading platform

cold-drawn seamless-steel column for maximum bending stiffness, flawless structural strength

Figure 39 *Tail lift detail*

The long-tried principle of electrohydraulic power lifting the platform smoothly and evenly up twin side columns is an established standard in tail-lift design.

Tail lifts suit van bodies, demountable body systems and drawbar trailer units. The seamless cold-drawn steel columns form a rugged structure with the overhead beam and the bumper bar, which together present an excellent fitting surface to match the vehicle rear frame.

General specification

Popular features (electrohydraulically operated from the vehicle's 12-V or 24-V batteries) included in tail-lift design include:

a   Platform, 1000 mm deep × 50 mm low profile, torsion-assisted for easy closure.

b   An overhead beam containing the main actuating mechanism of the lift, conveniently situated for easy service and accessibility, away from road dirt.

c   Rugged lift columns together with the beam provide a flat 'bolt-on' or 'weld-on' structure ideal for most flat rear frame bodies.

d Runners which carry the platform via a hinged joint allow the platform to be cantilevered from the rear of the vehicle without obstructing diagonal supports.

e Push-button controls with a second control station inside the vehicle or manual hydraulic release.

Options include other tail-lift platform depths, different work surface materials, ramps, safety rails, etc.

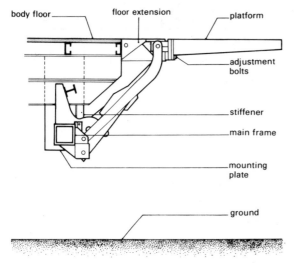

Figure 40   *Chassis-mounted rear-loading platform*

A typical chassis-mounted 900-kg 'HYD-A-WAY' rear-loading platform is shown in Figure 40. This type of tail lift or loading platform stows away conveniently under the truck body after use.

The manufacturer's instructions on selection and fitting of tail lifts should be strictly followed. The following are important factors to be stressed:

Overhang The single most important factor influencing the stress caused in the chassis frame by a tail lift is the chassis frame rear overhang and lift platform depth. This overhang should be kept to a minimum. However, a balance must be struck between the wheelbase and the overhang. An increase in the wheelbase and decrease in overhang will reach a limit at the point where the

front axle becomes overloaded and the payload has to be reduced. An increase in the overhang, to increase available payload volume, will limit the load capacity of the tail lift that can be fitted.

Rear axle The installation of an hydraulic load tail lift will increase the rear axle load of the vehicle both due to the weight of the lift when not in use and the load on the lift when in use. The resultant load on the axle must not exceed the maximum specified load in the driving condition.

Length/width On tail lifts mounted proud of the existing bodywork, the resultant vehicle length and width must not exceed the legal requirement.

Rear lights Legal requirements must be met on the position, separation and subtended angle of vision of rear lights when a tail lift is fitted. No component of the lift should obstruct the visibility of the rear lights.

Sub-frame It may be necessary to install a sub-frame on tail lifts with a large load capacity or with large chassis overhangs. This sub-frame should extend forwards over the rear spring hangers and have a 30° taper on the forward end.

Aerodynamic considerations

Air drag/power

Air drag accounts for nearly half the total power needed to drive an articulated truck at 96 km/h (60 mile/h). The lower the gross weight, the bigger the proportion of power that the air drag takes.

Fuel consumption

A 30% saving in air drag can mean a 15% saving in fuel consumption but this can only be achieved with efficient aerodynamics. Mixed fleets, different sizes, types and shapes of vehicle present problems of the type and location of aerodynamic devices. There is also the cost of installation to consider.

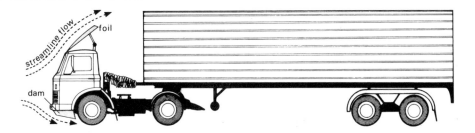

Figure 41   *Air drag reduction*

Research

The Motor Industry Research Association (MIRA) has completed a research programme on heavy goods vehicle aerodynamics and the results show that most ideas for smoothing out the air flow work and that some of the most simple attentions to detail can be the most effective. Aerodynamic tests were carried out in a wind tunnel on a scale model artic representing a Leyland Buffalo coupled to a 12-m van trailer.

Reducing air drag (Figure 41)

The Airvane airflow guide (Figure 42) has been designed and perfected by extensive wind tunnel testing and helps to smooth out the air flow over a vehicle. It is a lightweight aerodynamic device that can be installed easily on the front of any trailer or box van body. The reduction in air drag can lead to significant fuel savings – as much as 14.5% at 88 km/h (55 mile/h).

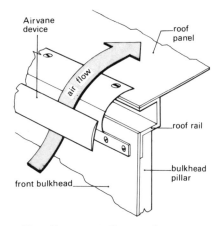

Figure 42   *Airvane airflow guide*

The Airvane is supplied in two models which fit any trailer or box body, and can be installed by one man in about one hour. Once the Airvane is mounted with simple threaded fasteners, no more maintenance or adjustments will ever be needed for the life of the unit.

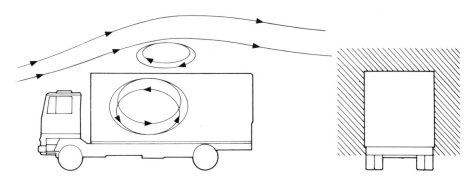

Figure 43   *Truck without Airvane airflow guide*

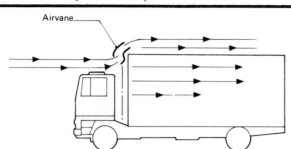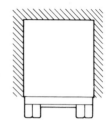

Figure 44   *Truck with complete Airvane installed*

A typical truck or trailer creates the kind of air turbulence shown in Figure 43 at highway speeds. The increased air drag actually increases the effective frontal area as shown, which leads to excessive power and increasing fuel consumption.

With a complete Airvane installed the air flow on the top and the sides of a vehicle (see Figure 44) is smooth, greatly reducing turbulence and air drag, which means reduced fuel consumption. Low drag will allow the vehicle to reach a higher speed with a given power output. By reducing the power consumption at any lower speed it makes available a greater power surplus that can give better acceleration. Only in the matter of braking does low-drag bodywork impair performance by offering less resistance to continued motion.

7 Chassis frame principles

General considerations

Some light commercial vehicle chassis have sturdy, parallel, box section steel frames providing vertical and lateral strength and resistance to torsional stress while others have strong ladder-type frames with cross-members and some variants employ cruciform cross-members for extra rigidity (see Figure 45).

Special Vehicle Order Departments (SVOD) must be consulted if an extension to the wheelbase or frame length is necessary to accommodate a special body. No welding is allowed on the frame without prior approval from an SVOD. Where approval on welding has been granted before commencing work, the electric leads of the generator/alternator and battery must be disconnected, otherwise extensive damage can be done to the electrical system. For arc welding, only dry welding electrodes with a lime basic shell (low hydrogen) should be used.

Rear overhang

The legal maximum for rear body overhang in a number of countries is 60% of the wheelbase, but chassis manufacturers often specify their own recommended maximum limits.

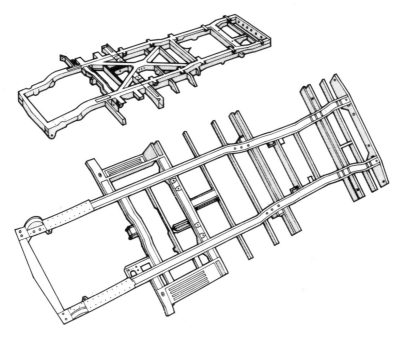

Figure 45   *Chassis frames for light commercial vehicles*

Axle loads

Axle loads must be considered in determining body length. In some cases where heavy duty suspension is specified, an SVOD may be able to approve a small extension to the rear of the frame. No alterations are allowed on the suspension, steering or brake system. The prior approval of an SVOD must be obtained before any chassis alteration.

Subframes – mounting

When subframes are required for a special mounting or body, they must be bolted to the mounting brackets already fitted to the chassis (see Figure 46). No spacer is required. The subframes should be made of U,H or box-type members in one piece to prevent peak tensions in the frame members. The subframe must run up to the back of the cab and have a clearance between subframe member and chassis side member forward of the front mounting bracket.

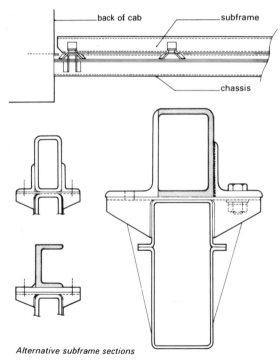

Alternative subframe sections

Figure 46   *Subframe mounting*

When mounting aluminium (or other alloy) bodies or subframes and brackets, zinc chromate paste or balata strip should be used to reduce electrolytic corrosion.

Channel-ladder type

Most commercial vehicle chassis frames are of ladder-type construction. The frame is not designed to be a rigid structure but to combine strength and flexibility. This allows the frame to 'weave' or twist (see Figure 47) and hence relieves stresses on springs and other chassis parts. Any body mounting practice that tends to stiffen the frame may cause the relocation of stresses to areas other than those intended in the original design.

Figure 47   *Chassis twist*

The frame consists of two side members bridged and held apart by a series of cross-members (see Figure 48). The side members support the load and the cross-members give torsional rigidity to the frame. Existing cross-members must not be used to support any body or equipment loads.

The steel channel section used for the side members (Figure 49) has a vertical web with a horizontal flange top and bottom. The web supports the downthrust of the body and payload and the flanges provide lateral support. Although the flange width is constant, the web depth may be varied along the length of the frame on light and medium trucks to accommodate the designed load distribution.

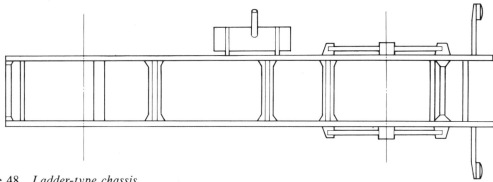

Figure 48   *Ladder-type chassis*

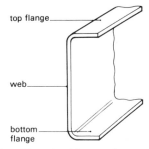

Figure 49   *Chassis side member*

Flitching

Both web depth and material thickness is varied for different load conditions. If the operational load conditions are such that greater resistance to frame bending is required, the use of external inverted L-section flitch plates, attached to the side member, is recommended (see Figure 50). These flitches have the effect of strengthening the chassis where the greatest bending moment or highest concentration of weight occurs.

Drilling of frames

If for any reason it is necessary to replace chassis frame rivets by bolts, holes in the frame should be increased to the next size up. For example, holes for 11-mm dia. rivets should be drilled and reamed to suit 14-mm dia. high-tensile fitted bolts.

When enlarging holes, sufficient metal must be left between the edges of any adjacent holes. The distance between the edge of holes must not be less than twice the diameter of the bolts or rivets used. Adequate distance must be left between bolt heads to engage spanners and power tools.

If new holes are to be drilled in the frame web, ensure that the frame is not weakened. As a general guide there should not be more than two holes in a vertical line down the frame web.

Holes drilled adjacent to spring brackets must have a specified minimum of metal between edges of holes or between edge of hole and spring bracket.

Holes should not be drilled adjacent to high-stress areas and must not be drilled in top and bottom flanges or near side member profile changes.

Existing holes in top and bottom flanges must not be bored out. If any new hole is drilled 25 mm from or closer to an existing hole, the latter hole must be plug welded.

Extensions must be secured with fitted bolts or cold rivets.

It is essential that the rivets completely fill the holes in the components.

No welding should be within 6 mm of any frame bend or sharp edge.

All extension components must be firmly clamped to side members prior to drilling any attachment holes. The extension components

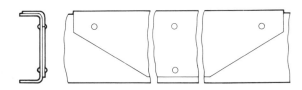

Figure 50   *Frame flitch*

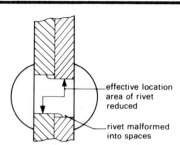

Figure 51   *Hole misalignment*

must be predrilled and used as templates for drilling side member attachment holes. Failure to do this may result in hole misalignment (Figure 51) causing stress concentration within the rivet/bolt, leading to failure.

Flitches

Chassis frame flitching is not permitted by some manufacturers. Factory-fitted frame reinforcement can be made available if required. Where granted by an SVOD the following important points should be noted when fitting reinforcing flitch plates:

1   Both ends of the plate should be tapered 30° to dissipate the stress along the side member web (see Figure 52).
2   When rivets are to be used as fixings, ensure adequate clamping of the flitch plate to the side member before drilling. Misaligned holes can cause high-stress points in the rivet and result in failure.
3   As an alternative to rivets, fitted bolts or huck bolts may be used as fixings. Fitted bolts should have a plain shank which is an interference fit in the hole.

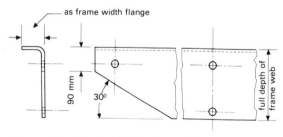

Figure 52   *Typical flitch plate design*

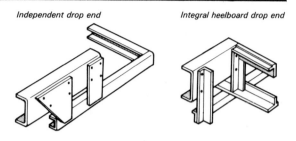

Figure 53   *Drop-end extensions*

Drop-end extension

'Drop-end' frame extensions (see Figure 53) are often required to provide a minimum loading height for tail lifts or low rear entry to the body. Sometimes it is necessary to reduce the length of the chassis to fit a drop-end extension. An additional cross-member must be fitted if the final overhang, beyond the end of the last cross-member in the original chassis, is greater than a specified distance set by the manufacturer. The additional cross-member may be fitted either to the end of the original chassis or the extension.

Frame-length alterations

No frame alteration of any kind is normally permitted on public service vehicles.

A good range of wheelbases are available from chassis manufacturers and correct vehicle selection could remove the need for frame-length alterations.

Frame-length alterations necessitate alteration of both brake pipe and electrical wiring harness runs. Pipe lengths may be altered using additional straight pipe and standard straight fittings. Additional electrical joints made must be waterproof and electrically sound.

Frame alterations fall into two categories, namely rear end or overhang alterations and wheelbase alterations (see Figure 54).

The epoxy-powder paint on frames, in the local area, should be removed without heat before welding to avoid production of toxic fumes. After welding, clean and repaint using zinc-rich primer and finish with air-drying alkyd-based paint.

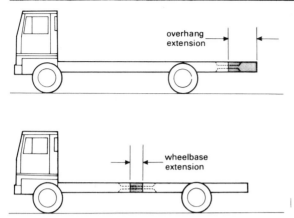

Figure 54 *Frame-length alterations*

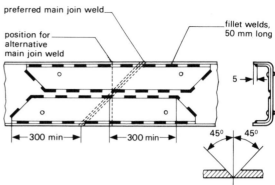

Figure 55 *Overhang alteration two-piece inserts*

The method of rejoining the side members is essentially the same. The extra channelling added to the side member must be of the same material specification and size as the original side member. The material specification will vary from model to model.

The alteration to a wheelbase or overhang will affect the split of weight between axles. The distributed axle loads must not exceed the legal axle weights applicable for the territory in which the vehicle is to operate and must never exceed the design axle load.

Chassis manufacturers often specify welding requirements to suit their particular frame material specification when alterations are proposed. An example is as follows.

Welding

Welding should be carried out to

a Metal arc to BS 5135 with electrodes to BS 639: E51–30B or semi-automatic to BS 2901 Part 1.
b Metal arc electrodes to ISO 2560 or semi-automatic to ISO 864.

Before any arc welding is carried out on the vehicle, all electronic equipment, such as alternator, regulator, radio, direction indicator unit and interior lamp should be disconnected.

Overhang alterations

When rejoining the side member sections, it is preferred that the main joint weld be made at 45°. If this causes problems of realignment of the side members, the alternaitve 90° weld may be made. In either case the overlap of the inserts should be at least 300 mm (see Figure 55). This method has the advantage of removing the need for the outside dimension of the insert channel to be exactly the same dimension as the side member channel. This eases the problem of insert material size selection and forming. If channel section material of suitable dimensions is available the insert may be made in one piece but must still be tapered at both ends (see Figure 56).

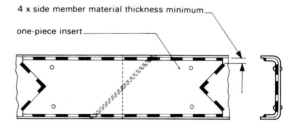

Figure 56 *One-piece insert*

Right-angle section inserts are necessary to provide additional load-bearing downthrust and lateral strength, i.e. to strengthen both web and flange. These inserts should be tapered at both ends to help spread the load and stop stress concentrations. The corner radius of the insert should be greater than the side member internal radius to give clearance. A gap of 5 mm should be left clear of weld along the edge of the frame flange.

The two mating edges of the side member that are to be welded should be chamfered at 45° prior to welding. It is good practice when placing the insert fillet welds on adjacent lengths of the inserts to alternate them. No welding is permitted within a distance of four times the side member material thickness from the corner radii of the side member.

The weld and surrounding metal must be allowed to cool by normal air-cooling. Under no circumstances should the cooling be accelerated by use of water or anything similar. After welding, the main join weld should be ground flat and flush on both sides. This is a vital part of the joining procedure and will greatly reduce the risk of fatigue failures.

Figure 57   *Wheelbase alterations*

Wheelbase alterations (Figure 57)

Rejoining the original side members to the added length of channel for a wheelbase extension, where two main join welds are required, is subject to the following conditions:

1 All the conditions specified for overhang alterations should be followed.
2 The method of rejoining described for overhang alterations should be used for wheelbase reductions as only one main join weld is required.
3 Dependent on the length of extension, it may be necessary to add cross-members to the frame.
4 No wheelbase reduction should reduce the wheelbase below that of the next shortest wheelbase in the appropriate range, without specific approval from the manufacturers.

5 No wheelbase alterations are permitted on articulated tractor units, some van chassis and coaches.

Change in turning circle

An alteration of the wheelbase of a vehicle will alter the turning circle. A wheelbase extension will increase the turning circle radius and a reduction will reduce the radius.

To assess the effect of a wheelbase alteration, the following formula calculates the approximate minimum circle radius for a rigid chassis truck, defined as the minimum turning radius of the outside front wheel:

Minimum turning radius $= W/\sin L$

where W is the wheelbase and L the maximum lock angle. The lock angle of the outside wheel should be used. Thus, if the wheelbase is 3810 mm and the lock angle 30°, then

$$\text{Minimum turning radius} = 3810/\sin 30°$$
$$= 3810/0.5$$
$$= 7620 \text{ mm}$$

To assess the effect of a wheelbase alteration, the following formula may be applied:

$$R_2 = R_1(W_2/W_1)$$

where R_2 is the new turning radius, R_1 the old, W_2 the new wheelbase and W_1 the old.

Prop-shaft lengths

An alteration of the wheelbase will necessitate changing the prop-shaft, and chassis manufacturers give general guides to maximum lengths of prop-shaft from universal joint to universal joint or universal joint to support bearing. Typical examples are

Shafts up to 70 mm dia.	Maximum length 1500 mm
Shafts up to 90 mm dia.	Maximum length 1700 mm
Shafts up to 110 mm dia.	Maximum length 1950 mm

If the shafts need to be extended beyond the manufacturer's specified limits, then two or three colinear shaft systems should be installed together with one or two intermediate support bearings. The angles between central axes of prop-shafts in a multi-shaft drive line and the number of shafts and joints in the line are crucial design considerations which affect both noise and vibration. As a general principle when the original prop-shaft system is altered the new angles should be kept as close as possible to those in the original system. In all cases it is good practice to keep drive-line angles to a minimum, but not zero as this can cause joint failures.

8 Body construction in aluminium

Economic advantages

The main economic advantages of using aluminium alloys for vehicle body construction are:

1 *Economy* in time and labour in assembly. Saving in assembly time is possible where, for example, one extrusion can be designed to do the job of several separate sections.
2 *Reduced maintenance charges* arising from the excellent durability of the materials. Aluminium alloys, due to their resilience, have a high resistance to impact loading; accidental damage is restricted to a small area.
3 *Resistance to corrosion.* The long service life of aluminium ensures minimum replacement.
4 *Reduction in unladen weight.* In commercial vehicles, a reduction in unladen weight can often mean increased load-carrying capacity. Tyre wear and fuel consumption are also improved when a vehicle is running empty.

Aluminium in contact with other materials

Aluminium and its alloys have excellent durability. This is due to the presence on the surface of an oxide film which is hard and strongly adherent. Furthermore, the film is remarkably inert. If disrupted it reforms immediately in contact with air.

All metals normally used for constructional purposes are affected to a greater or lesser degree by humidity in the atmosphere. Aluminium, however, by virtue of the protective oxide film, exhibits a very marked resistance in such circumstances. Normally the thickness of the film increases upon exposure, giving the metal a characteristic silver grey patina which can be preserved in appearance by regular washing to remove adherent particles of atmospheric grime.

In contaminated atmospheres, however, such as may occur in industrial areas, the metal assumes a darker grey patina. This change in surface appearance is characteristic of the metal and should not be regarded as detrimental to its strength. The weathering effect is more rapid at the outset and the action diminishes with time.

The normal behaviour of the metal can, however, be affected chemically or electrochemically by contact with certain other substances. Generally speaking, chemical action only takes place in the presence of moisture. It is therefore highly important in designing an aluminium structure to avoid moisture traps. Not only should these be eliminated as far as possible at the design stage, but care should also be taken to avoid their introduction during fabrication. Moisture traps may take the form of channels or pockets where water can accumulate and, by a simple rearrangement of a joint, can often be avoided. If such a change in design is not possible, then drainage holes, of sufficiently large diameter to avoid clogging, should be provided. Alternatively, filling the pocket with mastic or bitumen may be the simplest solution.

The most common form of moisture trap is the crevice; this occurs frequently in riveted structures. Provided the fit-up between the panelling and stiffener, for instance, in a vehicle body, is good, a coat of zinc chromate primer applied to the adjoining surfaces before assembly will give adequate protection. Bituminous paint is preferable, however, on such a joint in an insulated or refrigerated body as it will also provide a vapour seal.

Wood members attached to aluminium are more likely to give rise to crevices as a result of warping or shrinkage and a better remedy is required. It is recommended in this case that a zinc chromate jointing compound be applied in the joint and this will have the additional effect of preventing attack by any natural acid that may be present in the wood.

Where felt or other fibrous and absorbent insulating material is used between timber framing and aluminium panelling, the aluminium should be protected by a zinc chromate jointing compound or tape. It is also advisable to paint the timber with bituminous or aluminium paint.

Electrochemical or galvanic action takes place when two dissimilar metals are in contact in the presence of an electrolyte. Direct contact between aluminium and metals such as copper, brass and iron can give rise under wet conditions to a preferential attack of the aluminium. This form of attack can be prevented if the two metals are electrically insulated at the contacting surfaces. This can be accomplished by applying zinc chromate jointing compound to the areas of contact before assembly. Alternatively zinc chromate impregnated tape may be used. The tape should be cut slightly wider than the area of joint to avoid possible bridging of the insulation. Another satisfactory method, in the case of aluminium/steel connections, is to spray the steel with pure aluminium.

The greatest care must be taken to avoid contact between aluminium and copper or its alloys. The metals must be completely separated by non-absorbent washers, gaskets or bushes of an insulating material such as Tufnol or neoprene.

Brass pins or screws should not be used for attaching aluminium alloy panels to timber framing. Galvanized or cadmium-plated steel screws should be used for this purpose, and they should be dipped in zinc chromate paint before use.

Where dissimilar metals such as alloy (aluminium) brackets and steel side members are in contact, zinc chromate paste should be applied to the faces to minimize electrolytic corrosion. Balata strip can be used as an alternative.

Joining

Riveting and bolting

It is recommended that rivets for joining aluminium alloy components should be made from NR6 or HR30 material, both alloys being suitable for cold-driving. Rivets made from copper-bearing aluminium alloys are not recommended owing to their somewhat lower resistance to corrosion. It is normal practice to use rivets with a diameter of one to three times the thickness of the thinnest member through which they pass. Rivets are usually pitched at from three to six times their diameter. The pitch may be increased by an amount depending on the thickness of the

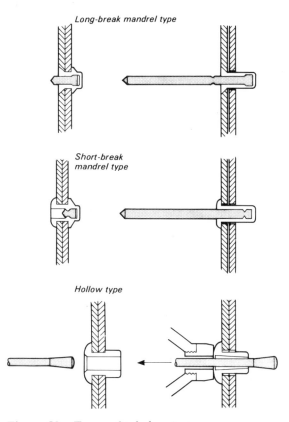

Figure 58 *Types of tubular rivet*

materials being joined and the need to avoid separation of the sheets between rivets. It is recommended that the distance from the edge of the material to the centre of the rivet hole should be not less than twice the rivet diameter. Aluminium alloy solid rivets are available with round, pan, mushroom, flat and countersunk heads as detailed in BS 641. Various types of tubular rivets designed for manipulation by one operator and permitting a very high rate of driving can also be obtained (see Figure 58).

Bolts of stainless steel, mild steel or aluminium alloy may be used and should be fitted with nuts of a self-locking type. Steel bolts, nuts and washers should be either cadmium plated or sherardized. Another type of fastener which may be used is the 'Huckbolt' (Figure 59). This type of bolt has a positively locked collar which makes it vibration-proof. The bolts and collars are made of aluminium alloy or alternatively in cadmium-plated steel.

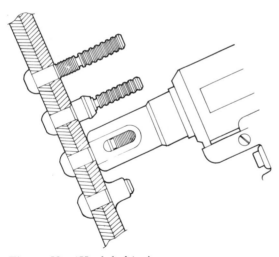

Figure 59   *'Huck-bolting'*

The Huckbolt fastening system has the following advantages:

1 Design and construction are such that a high pull-through and permanent clamp force is ensured by automatically pulling the sheets of the joint together and locking them with a high, uniform, predictable preload.

2 The high-tensile and shear strength of the installed bolt provides a joint with high resistance to vibratory loosening, permanent under all operating conditions.

3 Since no human factor is involved, the fasteners can be simply, uniformly and speedily installed – at a rate as high as 25 per minute by one or two semi-skilled operators.

4 The installation cycle is quiet, thus eliminating noisy rivet hammers or air-impact wrenches and providing a safe and pleasant working environment.

5 Element proofing through the bolt's excellent sealing qualities is important; the tension pre-load properties inherent in the design help to prevent water seepage and corrosion.

6 The bolt can be quickly and easily removed when necessary with a hand- or power-operated collar cutter.

7 The fastening system does not damage the work surface on application or removal.

Welding

Sound reliable welds of aluminium alloys can readily be made by the two inert gas welding processes: metal-inert-gas (MIG) and tungsten-inert-gas (TIG). No flux is needed with either process and post-weld cleaning is therefore avoided. It is important to note that in non-heat-treatable alloys the annealing effect in the heat-affected zone near the weld takes away some of the strength imparted to the material by cold-working (work-hardening). In heat-treated alloys the heat of welding causes a change in the metallurgical structure and the alloy may revert to the annealed condition in the heat-affected zone.

Finishing

Anodizing

Anodizing is an electrolytic process that thickens the natural oxide film found on the surface of aluminium. The anodic coating is a hard, dense and transparent or translucent layer on the aluminium surface which protects and preserves the appearance. The coating when first formed is porous allowing a range of colouring agents to be absorbed and producing a decorative finish. Many of the colours obtained are extremely light-fast.

Painting

Many aluminium alloy vehicles are left unpainted, the natural appearance of the metal being aesthetically pleasing and easy to maintain. Occasions arise, however, when a finish other than that of the bare metal is required, usually for identification or decorative effect.

Before painting, the metal should first be degreased. On small components this can be carried out by immersion in a trichloroethylene degreasing bath. Items too large for such treatment should be swabbed with a mixture of white spirit and light solvent naphtha in equal quantities by volume. Trichlorethylene should never be used for hand cleaning as it has anaesthetic properties.

After degreasing, metal surfaces should be etched or roughened to provide a key for the adhesion of the paint. This can be effected by using one of the many chemical treatments, etch or wash primers; or by scouring with emery, wire wool or pumice, followed by a cold wash to remove all abraded particles and dust.

A priming coat should then be applied. Zinc or barium chromate primers are very widely used for this purpose. Copper, graphite, lead or mercury bearing primers should not be used as these materials are unsuitable for use with aluminium.

After priming, the usual undercoats and finishing coats are applied. For these, cellulose or any of the paint systems normally used on vehicles can be employed but, as with primers, paints containing copper, mercury, lead or graphite powder should not be used. Painting may be carried out by spray, brush or dipping, no special equipment or techniques being required.

Lacquers

The original appearance of a body may be preserved by the use of lacquers. There are a number of proprietary brands on the market, each differing in formulation. It is, therefore, advisable to obtain the manufacturer's recommendations on pretreatment before applying a particular brand of lacquer.

Cleaning and maintenance

The maintenance required on an aluminium body will be negligible provided that the strength of the members and fastenings is adequate for the operating conditions of the vehicle and the body is protected from contact with dissimilar metals and those materials which have a deleterious effect.

Nevertheless, regular inspection of the vehicle body should be carried out to ensure that all fastenings, such as self-locking nuts and rivets, have not loosened as a result of vibration of the body and that unsuspected traps for moisture have not been built into the design during the vehicle's construction.

Moisture traps should be avoided, but where these do occur immediate steps must be taken to ensure that such traps have been thoroughly cleaned and dried before they are sealed.

The use of special fasteners, such as Huckbolts, for connecting floor planks to cross-bearers, etc., will substantially reduce the risk of loose fastenings. However, a regular check should still be made as a precaution, in case fastenings have worked loose.

Accumulation of road dirt and grime on unpainted body panelling may give rise to some surface pitting and washing down with warm soapy water at regular intervals is therefore recommended. Areas where surface pitting has occurred should be rubbed down with soap-impregnated wire-wool pads. Following this the panelling should be rinsed down thoroughly with clean water.

Local breakdown of paint finishes occasionally occurs as a result of poor preparation and pretreatment. If this happens, all loose paint should be removed and the underlying metal rubbed down with wire wool or pumice. The bare metal and surrounding paintwork should be washed with cold water and allowed to dry. New paint may then be applied.

Standard temper conditions

Following the alloy number is a symbol showing the condition or temper. The symbols are those of the British Standards Institution system of temper designation, and have the following meanings:

M As-manufactured, i.e. as rolled, without deliberate work-hardening to specific temper and without any form of heat treatment.

O Annealed, soft.

H2, H4, H6, H8 These are the four tempers (previously known as $\frac{1}{4}$H, $\frac{1}{2}$H, $\frac{3}{4}$H and H) to which aluminium and the non-heat-treatable alloys may be work-hardened by rolling or drawing. A particular alloy is not necessarily available in all four tempers.

TB Solution heat-treated only (previously W).

TF Solution-treated and subsequently precipitation-treated (also known as 'fully heat-treated', previously WP).

The standard sheet/plate alloys and tempers are given in Table 2.

Extrusions

Most of the members used in aluminium bodies of riveted or bolted construction are produced by the extrusion process; hot plastic metal is forced under pressure through a steel die to form a section of the required shape in lengths of 20 m or more. The process permits the economic production of a great variety of aluminium extrusions. In spite of the basic simplicity of the extrusion process and low cost of new dies for quantity production of an extrusion, the production of a section may be affected by its geometry, the alloy in which it is produced, any subsequent heat-treatment of the section and other factors. The principal alloys used in vehicle body building are given in Table 3.

Body construction – bump height

All chassis are connected to the axles and wheels by 'springs'. With rigid chassis this means that as

Table 2 *Standard sheet/plate alloys and tempers*

Alloy	Temper	Description
S1C S1C S1C	0 H2 H4	Commercial purity aluminium. For applications requiring very good corrosion resistance and formability, e.g. domestic cooking utensils, panelling and moulding, equipment for food and chemical processing. Low strength, easily weldable.
NS3	H4	A low to medium strength alloy with good ductility and corrosion resistance, good formability and readily welded. Applications include roofing sheet, domestic cooking utensils, containers and vehicle bodies.
NS4 NP4	H3 M	A medium strength alloy, with good ductility and corrosion resistance. Weldable. Typical applications include panelling for marine and road vehicles, pressings and containers.
HS30 HP30	TF M	The recommended alloy for structural purposes with good strength and general corrosion resistance. Applications include vehicle structural members, bridges, cranes and machine components.
NS8 NS8 NP8 NP8	O M O M	The strongest of the common non-heat-treatable alloys with high corrosion resistance and high ductility. Readily welded. Used for ship building and in welded structures. Suitable for low-temperature applications.
5005	H4	A low-cost alloy suitable for etching and anodizing with good quality uniform finishes matching well with HE9-type extrusions. The alloy is fine grained and readily shaped by pressing and forming. Corrosion resistance is very good and is further improved by anodizing. It is not susceptible to stress corrosion.

Table 3 *Principal aluminium alloys used in vehicle bodywork*

Alloy and condition	Application
Sheet, BS 1470	
SIC, annealed	For unstressed or lightly stressed
SIC, H8	applications: panelling, roofing,
NS3, annealed	etc.
NS3, H8	
NS4, annealed	Non-heat-treated alloys for low/
NS4, H4	medium stressed parts: panelling,
NS5, annealed	roofing. Also for pressings.
NS5, H2	
HS30, fully heat-treated	Heat-treated alloy for stress-carrying sheet and other purposes
Extrusions, BS 1476	
NE5, as extruded	Non-heat-treated alloy for moderate stresses
HE9, solution-treated	Heat-treated alloy for moderately stressed parts.
HE9, fully heat-treated	Suitable for decorative anodized finish.
HE30, fully heat-treated	General-purpose heat-treated alloy for structural parts carrying moderate to high stresses.
Castings, BS 1490	
LM4, as sand cast	General-purpose materials for
LM5, as sand cast	moderate stresses. LM5 is
LM6, as sand cast	particularly suitable for decorative anodizing.
LM8, solution-treated and fully heat-treated	For moderate/high stresses.

the body is loaded, it sinks on the springs and the top of the rear wheels rise above the top of the chassis members. The maximum rise above the chassis under any loading conditions is known as the 'bump height'; this is specified by the chassis manufacturer. The bump height must be cleared by the underside of the body, unless the floor is cut away to accept the wheels, using a 'wheel box'.

The underside of the body is lifted to the bump height by a variety of methods, e.g.:

1   By using longitudinal aluminium runners mounted on to the steel chassis with a timber or balata strip between the two, to insulate and prevent bimetallic corrosion.
2   By using pedestal mounting brackets between the steel chassis and the cross-members.
3   By using rectangular timber runners.

In addition, the cross-members assist in achieving the necessary clearance. When the aluminium longitudinals are continuous they should not be deeper than the steel chassis member, otherwise the body will become too rigid and cracking could occur in either the chassis or the body.

Flat platform bodies (Figure 60)

Aluminium is used extensively for the construction of flat platform bodies for reasons of strength, durability and lightness. Many of the less expensive light chassis have cheaper factory-built timber or steel bodies. The aluminium body is used, to a greater extent, at the larger end of the range and on the more expensive type of chassis.

As already described, the size of the longitudinal runner is, to a large extent, determined by the bump height. The floor is supported by cross-bearer channels, the lipped channel (Figure 61) or the 'J' channel (Figure 62) being used for most applications.

The only advantage the 'J' channel has is that floor fixing bolts are taken through the outstanding horizontal flange and the holes drilled to take the bolts through this flange do not weaken the channel in bending strength. The normal depth of a cross-bearer is 101.60 mm (4 in); 76.20 mm (3 in) depth may be used for light-duty bodies, i.e. building contractors. Cross-bearer spacing is generally at about 558.8 mm (22 in) to 609.6 mm (24 in) centres; 711.2 mm (28 in) should not be exceeded, unless the bodybuilders specify it. Also used is the British Standard 101.6 mm (4 in) × 50.8 mm (2 in) channel, normally for heavier duty applications such as brick lorries, brewery and dairy (churn-carrying) vehicles. In this case,

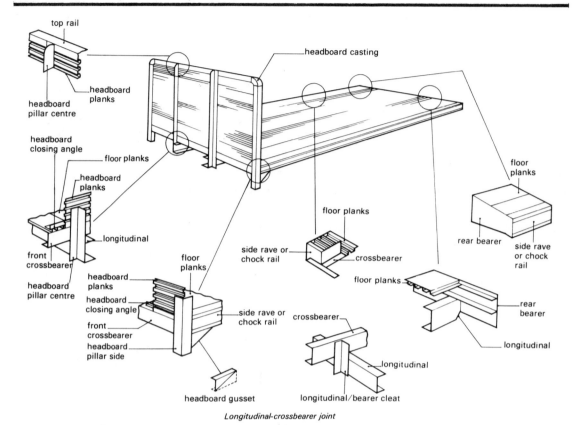

Figure 60　*Flat platform: general design*

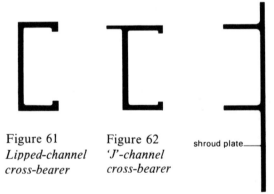

Figure 61
Lipped-channel cross-bearer

Figure 62
'J'-channel cross-bearer

Figure 63　*Rear bearer incorporating shroud plate*

bearer spacing should be restricted to 457.2 mm (18 in) to 508 mm (20 in).

A special rear bearer, incorporating a shroud plate (Figure 63) is sometimes used. The shroud plate allows bracket attachment to the longitudinals and also provides protection for the end of the floor planks. Bearers are solid riveted or bolted to the longitudinals using angle brackets or special mounting brackets (see Figure 64). The cross-bearers are capped longitudinally by side rave sections and are bolted or solid riveted to the bearers through the top and bottom flanges. Two types of side rave are available, one with a chock rail and one without (see Figures 65 and 66).

The chock rails assist with retaining the load, but make it nearly impossible to load and unload using fork-lift trucks unless deep pallets are also used.

The headboard is situated at the front of the body and behind the vehicle cab. This is a structural member or assembly because it has to resist the load moving forward and crushing the cab when the vehicle brakes are applied. For this

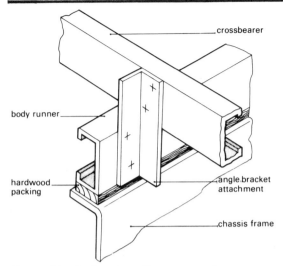

Figure 64 *Body runner/bearer attachment*

reason 76.20 × 76.20 mm (3 × 3 in) angles are used for framing, the bulkhead pillars are bolted to the longitudinals and the side or corner pillars firmly attached to the side rave using gussets. The headboard may be 10 swg (3.25 mm) sheet, but generally heavy-duty corrugated plank section (Figure 67) is used to provide strength. For the lighter range of vehicles, the light-duty corrugated plank section is an alternative.

If fork-lift trucks are to be used, cross-bearer spacing should not exceed 508 mm (20 in) and heavy-duty floor planks should be used with fixing bolts or solid rivets wherever a plank crosses a bearer. If the use looks to be very arduous or there is any doubt expressed about the ability of the

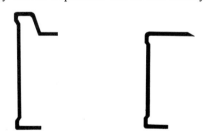

Figure 65 *Side rave with chock rail*   Figure 66 *Side rave without chock rail*

Figure 67 *Corrugated plank section*

floor to withstand the loads, it is recommended that a 10 swg (3.25 mm) plate is fitted over the planks.

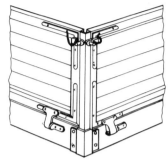

Figure 68 *Dropside truck body*

Dropside bodies (Figure 68)

A dropside body is a flat platform with hinged sides and tailboard, held in the upright position by fastening to short vertical pillars that are generally removable. The sides are normally made up by interlocking hollow plank sections (Figure 69) to build up to the required height and capping in picture frame fashion with a channel capping. Allowance should always be made to gusset the sockets to the bearers and side rave. Unless the side sockets are attached by brackets to a bearer, the body load will push outwards and put a permanent twist into the side rave (see Figure 70).

Vans

There are many variations to van construction and to detail them all would be too complex. The following highlights some of the features to look for in a specification when a customer says he has some vans to build (see Figure 71).

Selection of the underbody longitudinal is again largely dependent on wheel bump height. Many

Figure 69 *Hollow plank section*

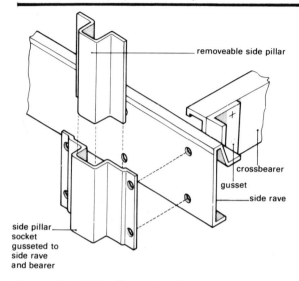

Figure 70 *Side pillar and socket arrangement*

vans, particularly parcel vans and furniture vans, have wheel boxes. This is done to lower the floor height and make loading by hand easier.

Remarks on the cross-members and floor planks are the same as for flat platform bodies with the exception that the superlight floor can be used with light vans, i.e. bakery vans. On the very light, 1500-kg vans the bearers are often built into the chassis in the form of outriggers and between chassis longitudinal supports.

The bearer capping section is now called a sill, mainside or bottom rail and is of different shape to a side rave (see Figure 72). It still needs attaching to the cross-members and provision has also to be made for fixing the vertical side pillars and the body side panels. Some bodybuilders use two angles running longitudinally along the top and bottom flanges of the bearers.

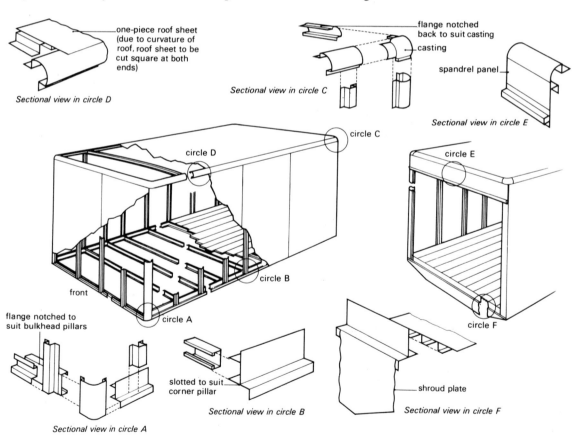

Figure 71 *Box van: general design*

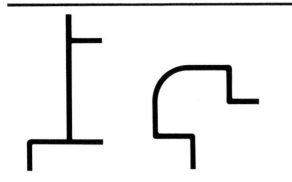

Figure 72   *Sill section*   Figure 73   *Corner pillar section*

Special sections are available for the front and rear corner pillars (see Figure 73). Selection of the front pillar depends on the type of van. The light-duty pillar is sufficient for parcel and bakery vans, the large pillar being more suitable for removal vans and semi-trailers.

Size and use of the van again selects the type of side pillar and roof stick. Bodybuilders and fleet owners vary in what they require and there are no hard and fast rules; 1500-kg vans would normally use a Z section, parcel vans a light top hat section and semi-trailers a heavy top hat section.

Pillar spacing is generally determined by panel size; there is always a pillar at the panel joint and normally one between panel joints.

Typical panelling (see Figure 74)

High vans, say over 2438.4 mm (8 ft) often have an intermediate longitudinal rail to reduce 'panting'

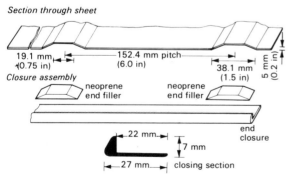

Figure 74   *Pannelling*

of the panels. This also applies to the roof where two longitudinals are necessary in between roof sticks and equally spaced across the roof.

There are always at least two vertical pillars spaced across the bulkhead and these again are normally joined on the longitudinals at the front of the body.

The longitudinal rail joining the side pillars and roof sticks is known as the cant rail. A very small cant rail is available for the light range of vans with the alternative of a flat roof or curved roof cant rail (Figure 75) for medium and large vans.

Figure 75   *Cant rail section*

The flat roof van is now in fashion, using either aluminium or GRP. Flat roofs normally have about 19 mm (0.75 in) set upwards in their roof sticks to stiffen the roof and stop panting.

A curved roof cant rail remains available, and so do the curved roof sticks. A single flange top hat is sometimes used at the extreme front and rear.

Various interiors may be specified: fully panelled, half-panelled and lashing rails or just lashing rails.

At the rear end there are again three main alternatives: double doors made up from top hat or Z section framing, with panels on both sides; full depth roller shutters; or roller shutter and tailgate or tailboard.

The rear corner pillar may be a single section or fabricated using a standard top hat and a light-duty corner pillar. Door opening dimensions and overall width will determine this.

Van bodies that are built over the chassis cab are called Luton bodies and the piece over the cab is the Luton, or Luton head. This type of construction is used with vans carrying low-density loads and it enables maximum body cubic capacity to be obtained.

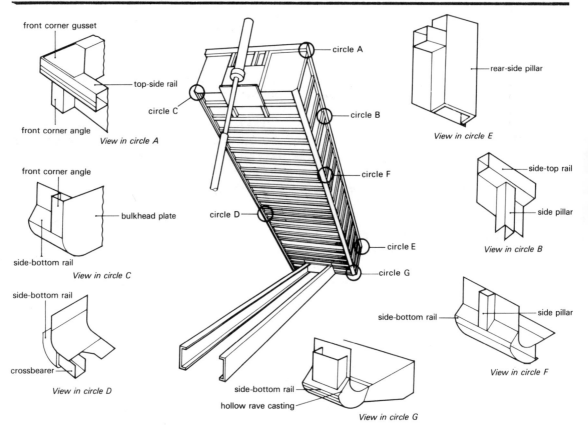

Figure 76 *Tipper body: general design*

Trailer vans

Basically there are two types of trailer van, the chassis van and the chassisless van. The chassis van is mounted on a trailer chassis, which is similar in function to a rigid vehicle chassis. The chassis van chassis normally has steel outriggers as part of its frame and therefore does not require cross-bearers. The body is built along similar lines to a normal rigid van body except that stronger sections are used for the framing because trailer vans are generally large vans.

The chassisless van is of specialist design; it does not have a chassis frame and all of its load-imposed stresses are carried by the body structure. Bearers, side pillars and roof sticks are spaced at less than 457.2 mm (18 in) centres.

Tipping bodies (Figure 76)

There are many types of tipping body, ranging from the smaller builders' yard tipper, which is similar to a dropside truck, to a 40 cubic metre off-highway dump truck. There are six basic variations to be aware of: welded or riveted construction, chassis or chassisless, front or underbody tipping gear.

Over the years the material content of bodies has been reduced to a minimum and one of the main areas for further reduction in cost has been labour content in fabrication. The introduction of welded construction has helped to retain a minimum differential between aluminium and steel tipping body prices.

The difference between chassis and chassisless

tipping bodies is that a chassis tipper has full-length underframe longitudinal channel runners which take the load stresses and resist body deflection, whereas the chassisless type of tipper uses the body construction as a beam in the same way as the chassisless van.

With the chassis tipper, the longitudinal performs an additional function to that of the flat platform body or van longitudinal. The tipping body longitudinal is connected to the body hinges at the rear end of the chassis and the tipping gear at the front end. When the body tips, the whole body weight is taken by the longitudinals and they must be strong enough to withstand this load. The longitudinals are not required just to clear the body bump.

Because of the depth required with aluminium longitudinals to provide this strength and resistance to deflection, and consequently their high cost, steel longitudinals are sometimes specified.

All tipping body sections need to be tough: the floor structure has to withstand heavy use, with the possibility of loads of rubble being dropped onto it from excavator buckets at above-body height. The sides not only have to resist bowing outwards, due to load pressure, but also damage caused by, for example, the impact of swinging load buckets.

It should be noted that the main difference between the chassis and the chassisless tipping body designs, apart from the disappearance of full-length longitudinal runners, is the spacing of the frame members. Because the chassisless body acts as a lifting beam it is necessary to make certain that the beam is strong enough to take the load and resist deflection. It is also essential to avoid areas of high stress and distribute the stresses induced by tipping the body.

There are two main advantages for a chassisless tipping body over a chassis body: reduction in overall body weight and consequently material costs, and also very often a reduction in overall

Description	Type 1: Tongue and groove	Type 2: Lap joint		Type 3: Plank and capping section	Type 4: Corrugated
		A (plain)	B (hooked)		
	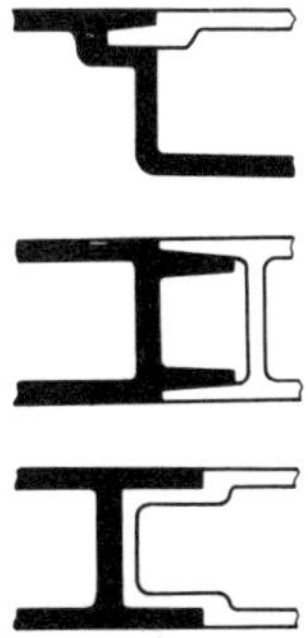	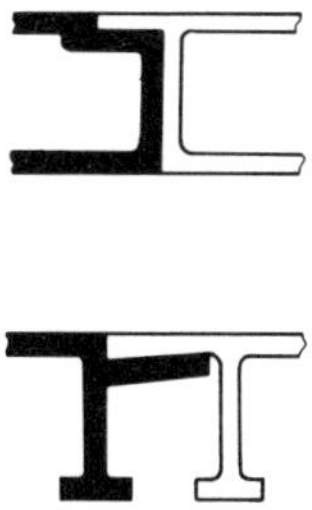	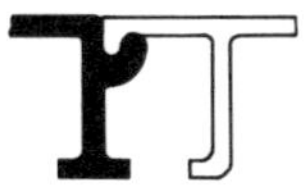	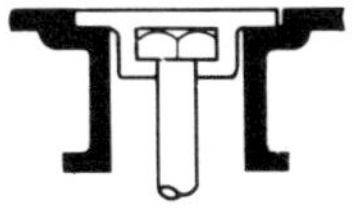	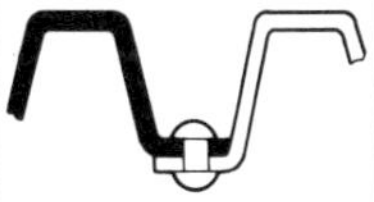
Assembly	adjoining planks drawn together with sash-clamps	adjoining planks drawn together with sash-clamps	self–locating; sash-clamps not necessary	adjoining planks drawn together with sash-clamps	riveted joint; sash-clamps generally not necessary
Performance under load concentrated on one plank	good; load distributed to adjoining planks. Planks cannot separate	planks may separate; must therefore be strong enough to carry load individually 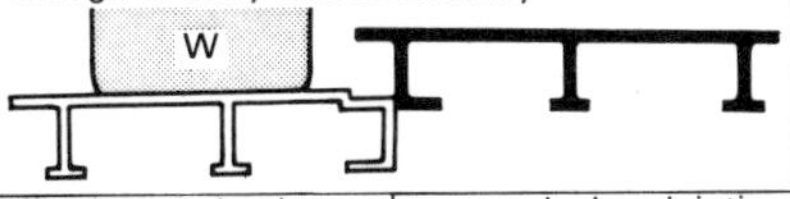		as for Type 2	excellent when adjoining planks riveted together between bearers
Water tightness	excellent; jointing compound more easily applied to top joint illustrated	difficult to maintain water-tightness even with jointing compound	very good when jointing compound applied in joint	difficult to maintain water-tightness even with jointing compound	excellent when adjoining planks riveted together
Ease of repair	planks adjoining damaged planks must be released	as for Type 1	damaged plank only need be removed	damaged plank and adjoining capping section only need be removed	rivets must be drilled out before removing damaged planks

Figure 77 *Characteristics of vehicle planking sections*

body height. This is a very important consideration because stability is one of the main concerns of tipping body operators, both in the tipped and untipped positions. However, with a rigid chassis it must be remembered that it still may be necessary to use short stub longitudinals to clear the wheel bump. The only advantage that underfloor tipping gear has over front end gear is that it allows the body space to go further towards the cab. Underfloor gear is generally used with the small bodies where body space is at a premium and stability and body height are not problem areas.

The underframes of bolted tippers are built up in a similar manner to platform and dropside bodies, only it should again be remembered that the longitudinals are used as structural members and not just to lift the body above the bump height. Cross-members 101.6 mm (4 in) deep are essential and a side rave is used to accept the hollow plank fixed sides, which are built up to the required body height. Side stiffness is provided by the heavier top hat section spaced at approximately 609.6 mm (24 in) centres.

It is essential that a substantial top rail is used; a 76.2 × 76.2 × 6.3 mm (3 × 3 × ¼ in) angle is recommended and this angle should also be used for the corner pillars.

Chassisless construction is not normally used with bolted and riveted tippers.

Sometimes body-builders want to use chassisless construction with dropside tipping bodies. This is not recommended because sufficient strength cannot be put into the underframe and the dropsides do not contribute to the overall body strength.

Aluminium planking sections

There is a wide range of aluminium planking sections for flooring headboard, sideboard and tailboard applications. Their characteristics are more conveniently compared in tabular form as shown in Figure 77.

9 Light van and platform variations

Box and Luton type bodywork on chassis cab units

When designing Luton and box bodies on chassis cab units, maximum permissible axle loadings must be observed and special consideration given to front axle loading, especially on Luton-bodied chassis. An SVOD heavy-duty front axle may be needed in certain cases.

Construction of the body must conform to local legislation although it is recommended that specified maximum dimensions are observed (see Table 4). Should it be necessary to exceed the limits for special-purpose vehicles, prior approval must be obtained from the chassis manufacturer.

Special consideration must be given to the body front mounting, where there is normally a high stress loading.

The front body or bulkhead loading must be transmitted firmly onto the front mounting brackets of the chassis and not rest on the chassis frame side member (see Figure 78).

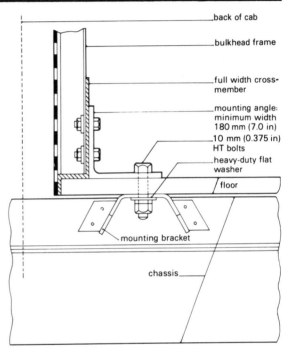

Figure 78 *Typical mounting attachment for a van body*

Table 4 *Typical examples of specified maximum dimensions*

	Maximum dimensions (mm)	
Wheelbase	2692	2997
1 Centre-line of rear axle to rear end of body	1035	1468
2 Top of chassis to top of roof	2336	2336
3 Width over body panels	1981	2134
4 Length over Luton head, mean interior	1067	1067
5 Minimum cab to body gap	25	25

The standard cab sheet metal work should not be used as a load-bearing structure to support the bodywork. Sufficient strength must be built into the front of the body to withstand the weight of the payload during rapid braking of the vehicle.

The diesel engine option will increase the front axle kerb weight, so in certain cases it may be necessary to restrict the front seating to one passenger only.

A notice should be fixed to the facia panel in the driver's compartment to display the maximum load that can be carried in the Luton head when the vehicle is uniformly loaded to maximum

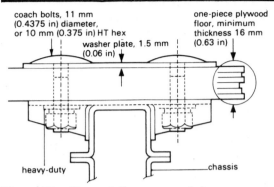

Figure 79   *Plywood floor mounted direct to chassis*

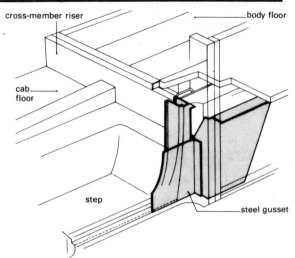

Figure 81   *Attachment of chassis front end frame to body frame*

permissible GVW. Where a one-piece plywood floor is to be mounted direct onto the mounting brackets on the chassis, the front and rear body mountings must be built into the front and rear body framework (see Figure 79).

Van bodywork on chassis windshield/cowl units (Figure 80)

This type of body will be required where light bulky loads are to be carried and easy access is necessary between the driver/passenger compartment and payload area. Points to note:

1   Maximum recommended axle loadings must be observed and the extra body weight carefully considered when establishing the maximum permissible payload.
2   The front of the body must be supported by the mounting brackets already fitted to the chassis and must not be carried by the floor of the chassis windshield or cowl.

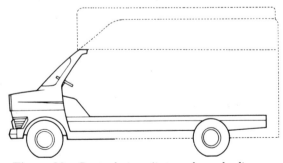

Figure 80   *Pantechnicon/integral van bodies on chassis windshield cowl units*

3   It will be necessary to attach the cab compartment floor and step well to the body by use of gussets (see Figure 81).
4   A minimum amount of welding should be employed when attaching the front end metalwork to the body.
5   No welding should be carried out on existing enclosed box sections.
6   When possible, standard production makers' doors, hinges, glass and glazing rubbers should be used.
7   Doors must be effectively sealed against dust and rain.
8   Forward vision and wiped windscreen area should not be impaired where a non-standard windscreen glass has been fitted. All windows must be of safety glass.
9   Where possible the driver's area of vision and defrosting should match that of the standard production van.

Mounting bodywork on chassis windshield/van floor units

This chassis is available on special application where body and equipment mounting approval has been granted by SVOD. The 'chassis' is desirable for special bodies such as coachbuilt ambulances and motor caravans that require the standard van floor height.

Mounting methods will be controlled by the type of body design and construction. Certain design objectives should be observed and are summarized as follows:

1 The van floor unit must be reinforced by the body structure.
2 The structure of the coachbuilt body must replace the strength and rigidity of the standard van body (see Figure 82).
3 Conventional structural members should form the basis of the body design and should include roof side rail, waist rail and rear door ring, strongly bracketed together.
4 The side panels of the van floor unit must be reinforced at the bottom edge.
5 Extension brackets for body mounting should be fitted in line with cross-members of the van floor unit.
6 The side structure must incorporate two fixing heights for pillars, at the van floor height and level with the bottom edge of the floor side panels.
7 Rear end loads should be distributed across the width of the van floor.
8 Welding to the van floor unit is not permitted, without the prior approval of SVOD.

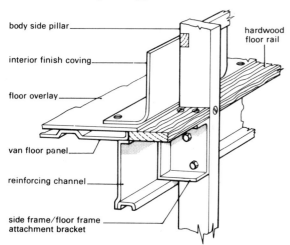

body side pillar

hardwood floor rail

interior finish coving

floor overlay

van floor panel

reinforcing channel

side frame/floor frame attachment bracket

Figure 82 *Typical section of side frame attachment to side member of chassis van floor unit*

This type of 'chassis' can be adapted for a very wide range of specialized vehicle applications. This will involve conversion work by body builders and installation of various equipment and bodywork.

Of particular importance are the suspension and the correct weight distribution of bodywork and equipment between and over the axles. Uneven side-to-side weight distribution may cause a vehicle attitude problem that will be easily noticeable with the softer springing fitted on ambulances.

Although a large number of body variants and options is available, some changes and conversions may still be required by customers. It is essential that recommended methods and procedure be adopted.

Van conversions

Sliding roof (Figure 83)

The corners of the hole made in the roof must be left with a minimum radius of 12 mm. Failure to do this will result in racking. All roof cut-outs must be supported by a frame attached to additional or existing roof bows so that support is obtained from the roof side rails. As much of the original roof structure as possible must be retained.

A drain channel must be built into the framework to collect any incoming rain water, and adequate outlets must be provided to permit immediate drainage. Thick plastic tubes are recommended.

A properly fitting weatherstrip to close the gap between the original and sliding roof is essential. A water test is recommended to ensure that all cutouts are properly sealed. Any leaks should be corrected and the installation retested after the vehicle has been allowed to dry.

All sharp edges should be avoided or safely covered. In some countries legislation controls the design of the body interior protrusions. The operating handle of the sliding roof should be recessed for safety.

The outer skin of the sliding roof should have

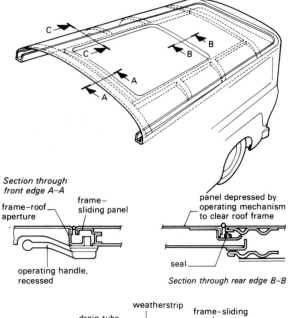

Section through front edge A–A

frame–roof aperture

frame–sliding panel

operating handle, recessed

panel depressed by operating mechanism to clear roof frame

seal

Section through rear edge B–B

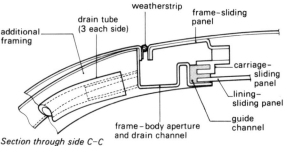

additional framing

drain tube (3 each side)

weatherstrip

frame–sliding panel

carriage–sliding panel

lining–sliding panel

guide channel

frame–body aperture and drain channel

Section through side C–C

Figure 83   *Sliding roof panel: typical sections*

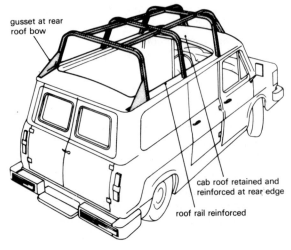

gusset at rear roof bow

cab roof retained and reinforced at rear edge

roof rail reinforced

Figure 84   *Roof reinforcement*

the same contour as the original roof. A smooth surface is mandatory to prevent whistling noises, especially at high speed.

High roof (Figure 84)

When a large hole is cut in the roof of a standard van, additional reinforcements may be necessary to provide longitudinal stability at the top of the side frame:

1 It is recommended that corners of the aperture framework are gusseted to the roof side rails.

2 High stress areas must be avoided. These can occur where panels have been cut away, especially when the roof and the side apertures are so close that the roof rain gutter rail is unsupported.

3 In all cases where panels or framing are cut away, the remaining structure must be reinforced (see Figure 85) so that the conversion does not reduce the strength and serviceability of the vehicle.

4 Wherever possible, the original steel roof panel above the driver's compartment should be retained and the rear edge should be supported by a roof bow. If it is essential to remove the panel, reinforcements must be used.

5 Extra strength must be built into the roof side rail where side loading doors are used with an elevated roof.

6 If the rear door aperture is to be modified to increase the height, then metal reinforcements and gussets should be used to secure the aperture frame extension to the existing door framework.

7 The prior approval of SVOD must be obtained before modifying the existing frame structure or body panels.

8 The completed conversion must be water-tested, any leaks corrected and the repaired area retested after the vehicle has been allowed to dry.

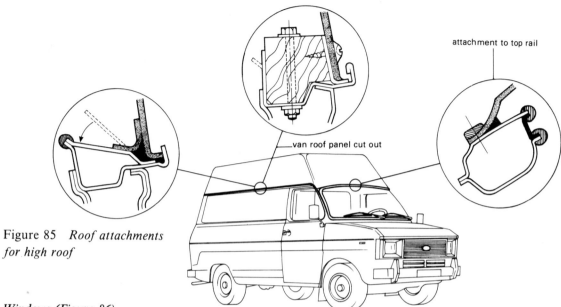

Figure 85   *Roof attachments for high roof*

Windows (Figure 86)

The side panel vertical joint and reinforcement must remain intact. A longitudinal rail should be fitted to prevent bulging at waist level. The rubber surround material used on the windows should be of the ozone-resistant type.

All windows must be adequately sealed with SVOD-recommended sealing compound. All glass must conform to the legal specifications of the country of destination. Regulations on the use of safety glass must be observed.

Standard glazing rubber specifications are available from SVOD.

Door clearance

When fitting additional doors, care should be taken to prevent water and light leaking in. Recommended maximum door clearances are as follows:

1   Between the edges of the doors and the nearest position of the surrounding body metal – 6.6 mm.
2   Door clearances should be parallel to within 3.0 mm.
3   The flushness of the door shall not exceed plus or minus 1.5 mm.

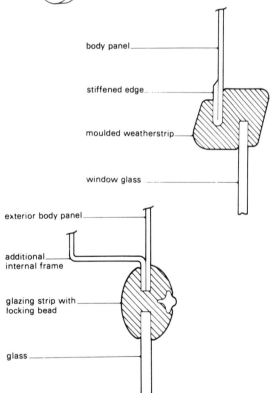

Figure 86   *Sections of side window installations for improved interior light in existing van*

Sliding doors and roller shutters

Special additional frames should be provided to give supplementary stiffness to the body when roller shutters are fitted. Flushness and clearance for this type of door will depend on the type of sliding gear fitted. It is important that clearance shall be parallel to within 3.0 mm along the margins of the door.

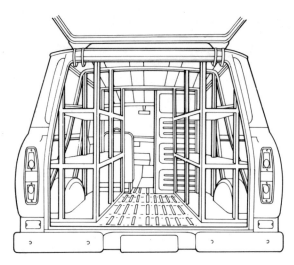

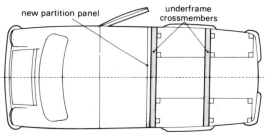

Figure 87   *Fitting partitions and racks*

Partitions and cab back parts (Figure 87)

Separate cross-frames should be provided for fitting new panels, especially when these are not located at standard body cross-members. The same principle applies for fitting racking.

There should be sufficient strength in the partition and its fixings to withstand the weight of the payload during rapid braking. Separate standard partition parts are available from SVOD.

If a bulkhead is to be fitted by a bodybuilder, it preferably should be located at the side pillar/roof bow location and securely attached.

Racking should be of rigid construction and be self-supporting. The racks should be attached to the floor with sufficient fixings to evenly distribute the payload.

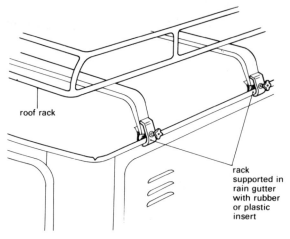

Figure 88   *Roof rack attachment*

Roof racks (Figure 88)

Roof racks should be supported by the lower section of the rain gutter and the mounting points should be in line with existing roof bows.

Paintwork should be protected by a rubber or plastic insert at each fixing point. If supplementary supports are used in the centre of the roof, additional roof bows must be provided.

The maximum recommended roof load is 100 kg; the maximum height of load above the roof panel 300 mm. Loads should be evenly distributed and the permitted GVW must not be exceeded.

Floor (Figure 89)

To level the floor surface, hardboard, plywood or rubber overlay may be used. For overlays which are not self-supporting, the troughs of the floor-

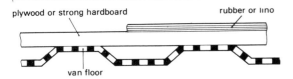

Figure 89   *Levelling of floor*

stiffening swages should be filled with composition board. Attachment of the floor covering should be made by using side strips. Where middle floor attachments are necessary, care must be taken to avoid damage to electrical and hydraulic lines when holes are drilled through the floor panel. The holes must be adequately sealed with a sealing compound.

Platform and float bodies on chassis cab units

The method employed to mount the body must avoid concentrations of stress which may produce failure of body or chassis components or both.

The load from the body should be applied through the mounting brackets which are fitted as part of the standard chassis frame side members (see Figure 90).

All supports should be attached to the mounting brackets with bolts, nuts and washers securely locked.

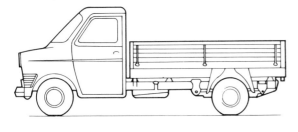

Figure 90   *Chassis mounting bracket*

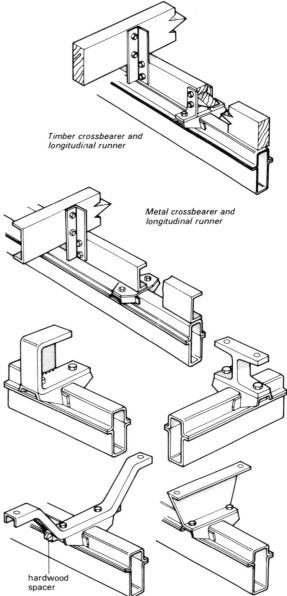

Timber crossbearer and longitudinal runner

Metal crossbearer and longitudinal runner

Examples of body-mounting pedestals to raise body to provide wheel arch clearance on flat-floor bodies

Figure 91   *Typical underbody construction*

Typical underbody construction (Figure 91)

Designs must ensure that:

a   The mounting brackets are not subject to either transverse or longitudinal racking.

b Sufficient clearance is provided between underbody and tyres.

c Diagonal bracing is provided to prevent lozenging when the body is pedestal mounted. In addition when dissimilar metals are in contact, such as aluminium and steel, zinc chromate paste should be applied to the faces to minimize electrolytic corrosion. Balata strip may be used as an alternative between body and chassis-mounting brackets.

d 'U' bolts are not be used for attaching the body to the chassis. They will cause damage to the chassis side members. In all cases the existing body-mounting brackets must be used.

Methods of stabilizing the underbody framing are shown in Figure 92.

Truck bodies with sheet steel floor

Recommended acceptance standards for truck bodies with sheet steel floor are as follows:

Floor alignment

1 Transverse floor members should be within ±1.0 mm each side of a mean straight line along their length.

2 On lines taken parallel to the vehicle centre-line the difference between the highest and lowest cross-member should not exceed 1.5 mm.

3 With straight lines taken longitudinally and transversely the floor sheet lowest point should be within 6.0 mm of the highest point. This must be a gradual variation over a distance of not less than half the distance between the main floor support members.

Rigidity

With the floor sheet under a load of 75 kg applied over an area of 100 cm² (an average person walking on floor):

1 Deflection should not exceed 2 mm.

2 Area of deflection should not exceed 30 × 30 cm.

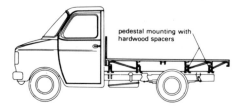

Underframe with diagonal stabilizers

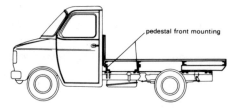

Underframe with short runners

Underframe with longitudinal stabilizers

Timber underframe with longitudinal runners

Figure 92   *Methods of stabilizing the underbody framing*

3 Panel should return to original level when load is removed.

Noise level

With the body mounted on a chassis the noise created by 'oil canning' should be no more than barely audible to a person walking on the truck floor.

Painting vehicles supplied in works primer

To ensure that locally applied finish coats of paint will adhere to the factory-applied primer, it is essential that the correct preparation methods are used. If incorrectly carried out serious defects can occur to the locally applied finish.

1   When a vehicle is supplied in primer paint only, the paintwork is incomplete and these coats alone do not offer complete or indefinite protection from the weather. Primer paints are relatively permeable to water vapour or moisture which, after penetrating the paint film, may quickly affect the underlying metal surface and weaken the adhesion of the primer paint to the metal. This can give rise to defects such as rust pimples or blisters. It may affect the adhesion to such an extent that the paint may flake from the metal. For this reason, vehicles supplied in primer should be finish-painted as soon as possible; in any case, within three months of delivery.

2   Primer painted vehicles should not be stored externally since it is not possible to use normal precautionary methods to safeguard them from the weather. It is inadvisable to apply protective wax to these primed surfaces, since great difficulty will be experienced in removing the wax completely before applying the finish paint.

3   When finish-painting these vehicles, the interior surfaces should be painted as well as the exterior surfaces, since condensation on the surface can give rise to defects.

4   When the surface is in good condition, a rubbing down with wet or dry abrasive paper (grade 360) using water to which a detergent has been added, followed by a thorough washing with clean water, should be sufficient preparation for a suitable base. After washing, it is essential that all the water is removed, preferably using clean chamois leathers. otherwise deposits in the water not visible to the eye may be left on the surface to adversely affect the durability of the finish. This is especially true if 'hard' water is used. In view of this, compressed air should only be used discriminately and should not be allowed to evaporate the water and leave the deposits behind. As a further safeguard, when the rubbed area is dry, wipe all the surface to be painted with a spirit wipe, methylated spirit and water, 1:1 by volume.

5   No matter what type of finish material is to be applied, once the vehicle has been allowed to deteriorate and rust has developed, all contaminated areas must be cleaned down to bare metal. Usually this can be achieved by using a high-speed sanding machine with a fine grit (120) disc. Broken edges of the paint film can then be 'flatted' and feather-edged using grade 360 abrasive paper, but to ensure complete cleanliness it is advisable to chemically clean any bare metal area with a rust-inhibiting and surface-conditioning fluid, closely following the manufacturer's recommendations. This will ensure that minute particles of rust which may be trapped in the pores of the metal will be neutralized. A coat of primer must then be applied to cover the bare metal before applying the finish coat of paint.

6   Before finish-painting wood surfaces 'dry scuffing', i.e. abrasive paper used without water, may be used, followed by complete removal of any paint debris. This procedure will not give such a smooth finish as the wet sanding method but avoids prolonged drying times and gives equal durability.

7   Both metal and wood surfaces should be completely dry before painting is commenced and in this respect an appearance of dryness is not sufficient. The vehicle must be left for 12–24 hours in a warm dry atmosphere unless forced drying facilities are available. If the vehicle is of all-metal construction then 12 hours should be sufficient but if part of the bodywork is wood then 24 hours should be allowed.

8   All oil and grease should be removed with a suitable solvent such as oil-free petrol or white spirit. Paraffin should not be used as it tends to leave an oil film on the surface. Before applying

the finish coats, remove all dust by wiping the vehicle thoroughly with clean tack rags, paying particular attention to any crevices. Where white spirit is used, care should be taken to reduce to a minimum contamination of rubber parts and appropriate fire precautions must be taken if petroleum spirit is used.

These instructions are intended as a general guide to finish-painting commercial vehicles supplied in primer. It is emphasized that the specific instructions of the manufacturer of the paint finish process used must be strictly observed if the best results are to be obtained.

10 Body and equipment mounting

General principles

Chassis frames are designed and stressed to provide maximum strength with minimum weight. A key factor in this strength is the flexibility of the chassis frame. The method used to mount the body must not adversely affect the flexibility of the chassis frame and must avoid any concentration of stresses which may result in failure of chassis components, body or both. A rigidly mounted body can cause the rivets in the rest of the frame to work loose. Points to observe are as follows:

1 The imposed loads from body to chassis frame must be applied to the side member at equal or near equal intervals along the chassis frame.
2 Frame-mounted body attachment brackets must not be welded to the chassis side members or bolted through the top and/or bottom side member flanges.
3 All attachment bolts must be secured with lock nuts or nuts with heavy-duty lock washers.
4 Body subframes and mounting brackets must be securely clamped to the frame side members before drilling the frame web or body runner for fixing bolts.
5 All brackets must be attached to the frame side member web by means of fitted bolts.
6 Where dissimilar metals are used such as light alloy and steel, zinc chromate paint/paste should be applied between the faces to minimize electrolytic corrosion. Where practical, balata strip can be used as an alternative.
7 Where it is necessary to shorten the vehicle frame overhang, it is essential that a chassis frame rear closing cross-member is fitted and the rearmost body-mounting brackets be fitted as close as possible to this member.
8 During the mounting of bodies it is essential to check for any foul condition relative to the electrical wiring and other electrical equipment, brake pipes, brake hoses and equipment and associated engine components.
9 It must be possible to detach bodies without disturbing or breaking any electrical or brake connections and pipes or any other vehicle equipment and components.

Centre of gravity

There is a point on an unbodied vehicle at which the mass is effectively centred, termed the centre of gravity (see Figure 93). If the vehicle is to be stable when cornering, the CG of the bodied vehicle should as low and as near the centre of the vehicle

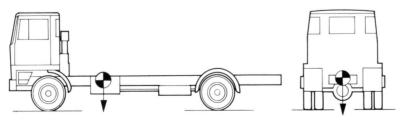

Figure 93 *Chassis/cab centre of gravity*

as possible. Any part of the body or equipment placed above the original CG will cause the new CG to be higher.

Raising the CG is inevitable when mounting a body or equipment but all possible steps should be taken to minimize this effect by mounting heavy parts of the body or equipment as low and as symmetrically about the chassis frame as possible.

Mounting on channel-section chassis frames

When a body is mounted on the chassis frame it is very important to transmit the load to the channel section in the correct manner. If the load is applied directly to the top flange (see Figure 94), stresses in the side member will be considerably higher than those predicted. This will influence the fatigue life of the frame.

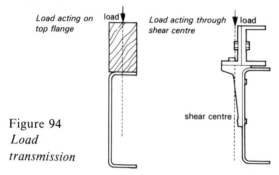

Figure 94
*Load
transmission*

To ensure pure bending and no twisting moments the load must be applied in a vertical plane through the shear centre, which lies outside the channel section. To achieve this, the body must be mounted on an outrigger-type bracket bolted to the frame web (see Figure 95). Suitable brackets are available from main dealers.

The outrigger bracket has a lip which should not extend more than a maximum distance of 25 mm over the top flange of the frame as this would restrict the frame in 'weaving'. This lip serves several purposes.

1 It forms a wider top surface to the bracket.
2 It partly relieves the fixing holes of direct shear load.
3 It acts as a spacer between top flange and cross-bearer (if used).

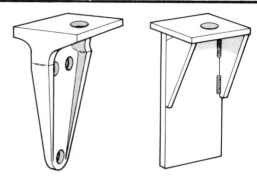

Figure 95   *Outrigger
-type body mounting
bracket (malleable
cast iron)*

Figure 96   *Fabricated
outrigger bracket*

Suitable outrigger brackets may be fabricated from 6 mm (minimum) steel plate (see Figure 96).

All brackets used must be fixed to the frame web using fitted bolts, 'cold squeeze' rivets or Huckbolts inserted into drilled and reamed holes to give an interference fit. Holes must not be gas cut.

On flitched chassis the mounting bracket should be used on the flitched section of the side member; it can be welded to the flitch-plate face. The lower fixing bolt should be well below the central or neutral axis of the frame web on all brackets used. The bottom edge of the bracket should be as near the bottom of the web as possible to prevent 'oil canning' frame failures. Brackets should be placed at approximately 914 mm (36 in) centres along the length of the body.

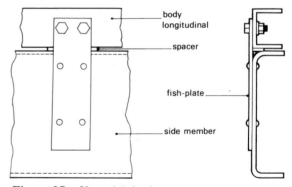

Figure 97   *Use of fish-plates*

Fish-plates

If the space available along the side of the chassis frame precludes the use of outrigger brackets, the body may be attached in these areas using fish-plates (Figure 97). The 25 × 6 mm section spacer must still be placed between the chassis frame and body frame and welded to the fish-plate. These fish-plates should be placed at approximately 914 mm (36 in) centres along the length of the body.

Cross-bearers

If the body is to be mounted on cross-bearers, they in turn should be mounted on outrigger brackets, ensuring that the cross-bearer does not bear directly on the top flange of the frame (see Figure 98). This method permits a lower body floor height.

Soft spacing material

Soft spacing material such as balata may be used as a vibration-deadening material on body mounts. It should be placed between the faces of the chassis frame bracket and the body-mounted bracket and will take up any slight misalignment of body brackets. It may also find applications in prevention of cab noise intrusion.

Mounting on box-section chassis frames

Some chassis frames are constructed from double top hat welded longitudinals with box-section main cross-members and a deep, multiple-flanged

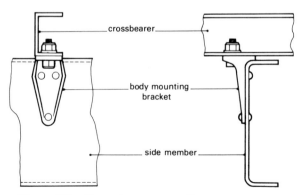

crossbearer

body mounting bracket

side member

Figure 98 *Cross-bearer mounting*

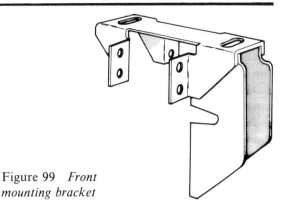

Figure 99 *Front mounting bracket*

rear cross-member. As the box-section is symmetrical in section, the load of the body should be transmitted to the frame symmetrically.

Front pair – mounting brackets

The front pair of body-mounting brackets (Figure 99) incorporating additional supporting buttresses are fitted on production and must be used when mounting a body.

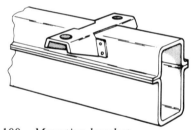

Figure 100 *Mounting bracket*

All other body mounts

Specially designed pressed-steel body-mounting brackets (Figure 100) are available through dealers and should be used for all body mounts other than the front pair. They should be pop-riveted to the side member and not welded. Heat application will mar the frame's strength. Each bracket has eight drillings to suit 6.35 mm (0.25 in) 'Monel' steel pop rivets and only this type of rivet should be used. When attaching the body to these brackets, both slotted top face holes of the bracket must be used. A heavy-duty plain washer should be placed underneath the slotted top face holes to

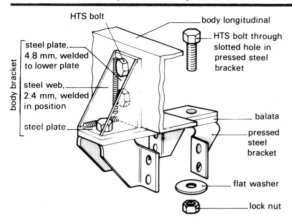

Figure 101   *Mounting body longitudinal*

ensure good clamping and spread of load. A strip of balata or similar material should be placed on the top face of the pressed-steel mounting bracket to take up any misalignment.

Body longitudinals

The suggested method of mounting body longitudinals, particularly of dissimilar metals, on the pressed-steel mounting brackets is shown in Figure 101. The fabricated body bracket should be pre-assembled and welded, preferably on a jig. A large flat washer, approximately 25 mm in diameter, must be placed between the two slotted bracket holes and fixing bolts. Body-mounting brackets should be placed at approximately 760 mm (30 in) centres along the chassis frame. This method is suitable for mounting wooden, steel or alloy longitudinals.

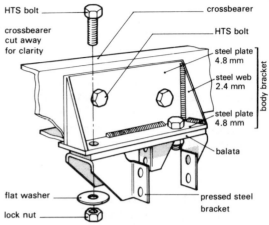

Figure 102   *Cross-bearer mounting*

Body cross-bearers

A suggested method for attaching body cross-bearers (particularly with dissimilar metals) to the pressed-steel mounting brackets is shown in Figure 102. As for body longitudinals, a flat washer, approximately 25 mm in diameter, should be placed between the slotted bracket hole and fixing nut. This method of mounting is suitable for wooden, steel or alloy cross-bearers.

Where areas of alloy and steel are in direct contact, zinc chromate paste should be applied to mating surfaces to reduce electrolytic corrosion.

Pedestal mounting

When a flat floor is required, necessitating the use of pedestal brackets between the chassis frame and

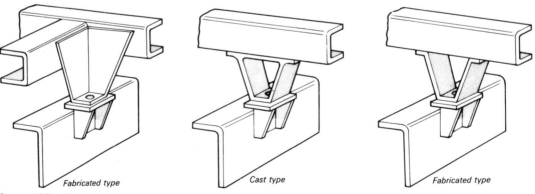

Figure 103   *Body-mounting pedestals*

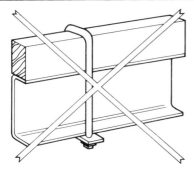

Figure 104 *'U' bolt mounting*

body understructure, longitudinal stabilizing must be incorporated within the body mounting system to prevent distortion of the pedestal mounts under braking loads. Pedestal brackets may be of the cast or fabricated design (see Figure 103). To ensure positive fore and aft location of the body, the rear pair of body brackets must have plain holes to match the corresponding chassis-mounted brackets.

'U' bolt mounting

The simple method of mounting the body – running a body member straight along and directly on top of the frame flange and fixing with 'U' bolts – is not recommended for rigid box-type structure bodies (see Figure 104). There are four very important design reasons for this:

1 The runner stiffens the frame, thus reducing the flexibility along part of the frame length. All flexing thus takes place in the uncovered length of the frame causing high stress levels in this section which could lead to metal fatigue and frame cracking.
2 The 'U' bolts holding the runners are often over-tightened causing the frame flange to buckle. Once buckled, the flanges have their strength greatly reduced.
3 Wood or metal spacers are often positioned between top and bottom flanges to stop the flanges from buckling. This causes local stiffening, loss of flexibility and high stress concentrations.
4 The fixing of the body relies on friction and high clamping forces with no positive location.

However tight 'U' bolts are fitted, they work loose or the wooden runners shrink and the body is then free to slide on the chassis frame.

Conditions of 'U' bolt mounting for platform and float bodies

This type of mounting should not be used where chassis component relocation or rework is necessary to fit the frame spacer or 'U' bolt. When fitting 'U' bolts, the following conditions should be strictly followed:

1 It is essential that metal spacers (see Figures 105 and 106) are fitted between frame side member flanges and adjacent to the inside leg of the 'U' bolt.
2 The spacers must be positively located by the 'U' bolt inner leg and must include a positive stop to prevent rotation about the 'U' bolt. A

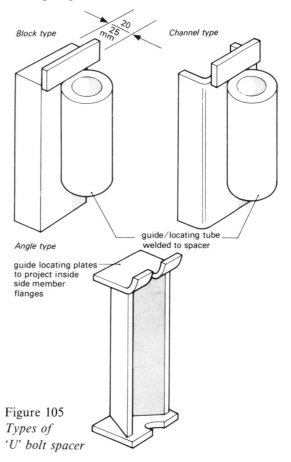

Figure 105
Types of
'U' bolt spacer

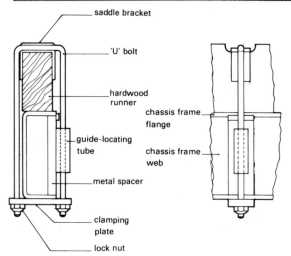

Figure 106   *'U' bolt spacer and fitting*

minimum clearance of 10 mm to vehicle service lines – brake pipes, wiring, etc. – must be maintained.

4   The 'U' bolt bottom clamp plate must be a rigid plate or casting of sufficient strength to resist bending within itself and thereby prevent bending of the frame flange.

5   The 'U' bolt legs must be as close as possible to the chassis frame web and flanges.

6   Wooden spacers are not acceptable due to possible shrinkage that would cause loosening of the body fixing.

7   The mounting must be secured with lock nuts or nuts with heavy-duty lock washers.

Tanker mounting

General principles

The mounting of tanker bodies is the most specialized of all equipment mountings because the torsionally stiff body can easily create local high stress points in the chassis frame. This applies to tankers carrying bulk liquids and free-flowing solids in containers of similar design.

The tanker body must be considered as a rigidly constructed vessel. It is essential that this construction be allowed to float on the chassis and that the vehicle chassis flexibility is not affected.

Flexible mounts must be superimposed between the chassis and the tanker or container body. Where a subframe mounting is not incorporated, a five-point mounting must be used with the odd mounting point located at the front of the tank.

Front, intermediate and rear mountings (Figure 107)

The single front mounting must be flexibly supported at the longitudinal pin by means of a cylindrical bush and flexibly supported at each end of the cross-member — which should be positioned as far forward as possible.

It may be necessary to restrict the amount of

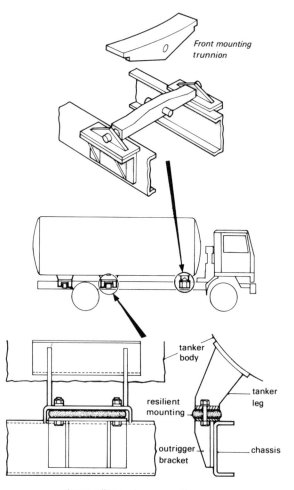

Figure 107   *Tanker mounting*

torsional movement at the trunnion by means of buffers. The intermediate or second pair of mountings must be located as close as possible to and in front of the rear spring front hanger brackets and the construction of the mountings must be similar to those used at the rear. The tank rear mounting feet must be attached to the chassis through a resilient mounting on frame outrigger brackets, located as close as possible to and behind the rear spring rear hanger brackets.

Mounting conditions

1 Since a small number of mounting brackets are used in comparison to the number required for mounting a truck body, greater strength must be designed into tank mounting brackets.
2 The vertical face of the outrigger brackets must extend to the full depth of the chassis frame.
3 Failure to achieve full-depth brackets could create an 'oil-can' effect on the chassis side member. This may cause cracking of the chassis frame web at the lower edge of the bracket.
4 Brackets should not be welded to the chassis frame and no holes should be drilled in the top or bottom flanges of the chassis frame.
5 All brackets should be attached to the frame using fitted bolts with lock nuts or nuts and spring washers. Simpler methods of resilient mounting, not incorporating a trunnion mount, can be adopted on a vehicle where the tank is able to flex, to a degree, without affecting the structure (see Figure 108).

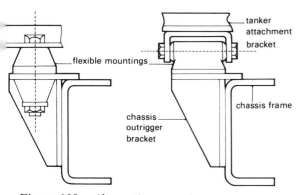

Figure 108   *Alternative mountings*

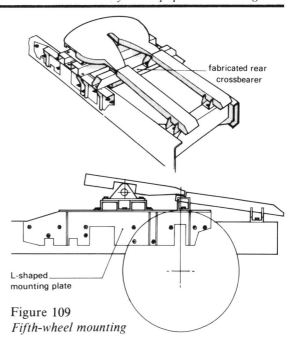

Figure 109
Fifth-wheel mounting

6 The centre of gravity on all installations should be kept as low as possible.

Consideration must also be given to the legal requirements applying to tankers used for carrying inflammable liquids and free-flowing solids or explosive loads such as liquid gas. The regulations may require that this type of vehicle is equipped with firescreen, special electrical equipment, screening of batteries, front-mounted exhaust plus screening and protection of cab rear windows. Options such as front-mounted exhaust system, insulated-return electrical system, battery isolation switch and relocated chassis equipment can be factory-fitted.

Fifth-wheel mounting

The basic supporting structure for fifth wheels has two L-shaped mounting plates bolted to the frame side members with cross-bearers between them (see Figure 109). The fifth wheel is mounted on the front pair of cross-bearers.

Lead-up ramps, if required, should be mounted on a fabricated rear cross-bearer and the rear cross-member, which must be reinforced on certain models. The L-shaped mounting plates have a similar cross-section to that of the standard outrigger bracket in order that the load be transmitted to the chassis frame correctly.

The following are important points to observe when mounting fifth wheels:

1 Fifth-wheel mounting plates should not be welded to the side members, or frame members mutilated in any way to accommodate the structure.
2 'U' bolt attachment to the frame should not be used.
3 Top or bottom side member flanges should not be drilled.
4 Support rails should extend well forward and rearward of the fifth-wheel king pin and be tapered at both ends to distribute the load along the chassis and avoid stress concentrations. Cut-outs should be made to avoid other components mounted on the side-member.
5 Articulation, swing radius and fifth-wheel height should comply with the Society of Motor Manufacturers and Traders recommendations and BS AU3 1970 or the recommendation applicable in the territory of operation.
6 Tail lamps will need to be repositioned to provide clearance for the trailer and to conform to legal requirements.
7 Dependent on the fifth wheel position and some trailer designs, it may be necessary to shorten the side member at the rear of the vehicle to provide clearance for the trailer landing gear. The amount removed should be kept to a minimum.

Tipper mounting

As a tipper body must be rigid to support the load when tipping, it is important to correctly locate the support brackets to avoid frame problems resulting from hammering (see Figure 110). The following points must be observed:

1 In the lowered position, the body must be supported on three points, two landing plates and one pivot bracket, each side of the frame.

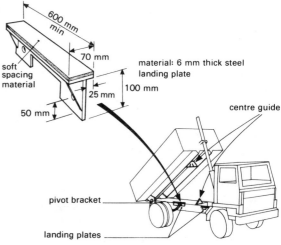

Figure 110   *Tipper supports*

2 The four landing plate support brackets must be substantial in design and load-carrying area. If they are not of adequate strength, the chassis top flange will take the load, resulting in frame damage.
3 The rear pivot must be positioned as close as possible to the rear spring rear hanger brackets.
4 Guide plates must be provided, preferably a central guide located on an additional cross-member. Under no circumstances should an existing cross-member be used.
5 Alternatively, substantial side-mounted guides can be used with the lower bolt well below the frame web centre-line (see Figure 111).
6 If medium or long wheelbase vehicles are used as tippers, they should only carry free-flowing loads and be used on firm, level ground.
7 Spill plates should be fitted to protect the gear box and the rear of the engine from falling rubble, etc.

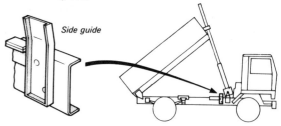

Figure 111   *Side-mounted guides*

8 A full chassis length subframe must be fitted to all chassis for three-way and underbody type of tipping gear and the subframe must be mounted as described earlier. It is permissible to shorten the rear of the frame to obtain the required tip angle where foul conditions occur (but this must not be done by flame-cutting).

Ram mounting

The front end ram gear should be mounted with a cast or fabricated pivot bracket of an 'A' frame design connected to the chassis frame side member web, using fitted bolts in existing holes (see Figure 112).

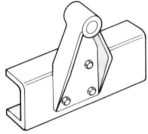

Figure 112   *Front end ram mounting*

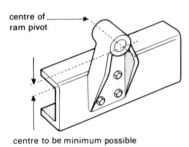

centre of
ram pivot

centre to be minimum possible

Figure 113   *Underfloor ram mounting*

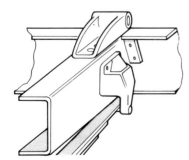

Figure 114   *Three-hole fixing, rear hinge mounting*

When fitting underfloor ram gears (see Figure 113), the pivot-mounting brackets should be secured to the chassis frame side member web as for front end ram mounting. The height of the pivot should be as close to the top flange of the chassis frame as possible and the bracket should provide a wide contact length to spread the load. Existing holes should be used wherever possible.

Rear hinge mounting

The rear hinge pivot-mounting bracket must be located directly above or immediately behind the rear spring hanger bracket using existing holes in the frame top flange and in the frame web wherever practical. Care should be taken to ensure that the rear of the tipper body does not, when tipping, 'dig' into the partially tipped load and create a tendency to lift the rear wheels, thus losing traction.

On certain models a cast or fabricated bracket with 'three hole' fixing must be used (see Figure 114). The rear light and mounting brackets may need to be relocated to clear the body on tip. On

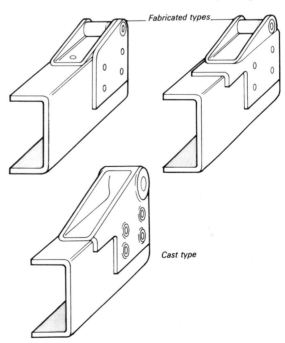

Fabricated types

Cast type

Figure 115   *Rear hinge mounting brackets*

others a straddle-type bracket (see Figure 115) must be fitted and should extend down the side member web to incorporate the rear lamp mounting-bracket holes. The existing single hole in the top flange must also be used. The rear lamp brackets must be remounted on the outer face of the hinge brackets.

Where front end twin rams are specified on certain tandem tipper models it is recommended that stabilizer struts be fitted (see Figure 116).

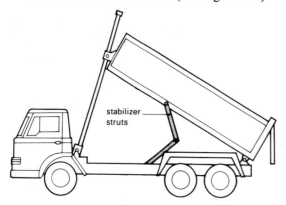

Figure 116   *Stabilizers*

Special-purpose bodies

Concrete mixers

Mounting of concrete mixer equipment requires very careful consideration because of its unusual weight distribution and the transfer of load that occurs when the drum is in motion. Incorrect mounting could lead to chassis frame failure. The equipment should be mounted on a substantial continuous subframe, tapered at the front to gradually reduce the section modulus. On some chassis the manufacturers specify that the length of the subframe must extend as far forward of the front spring rear hanger bracket as possible. On others, the subframe must extend up to the rear edge of the engine rear mounting cross-member. For 4 × 2 models, five pairs of mountings are normally used. The front and rear mountings are located as close as possible to the front and rear ends of the subframe, respectively. The third pair of mountings should be located immediately

forward of the rear spring front hanger brackets and the fourth pair of mountings should be located immediately to the rear of the rear spring rear hanger brackets. The second pair of mountings can then be positioned approximately midway between the front and third pair of mountings.

For 6 × 4 models, six pairs of mountings are normally used in similar locations as the single drive-axle models, with the additional pair of mountings located immediately forward of the bogie rear suspension central hanger bracket.

Method of mounting subframe (Figure 117)

Where insufficient room exists for outrigger brackets without relocation of chassis components, 'U' bolts may be used.

Flexible mountings

If flexing between the subframe and equipment is undesirable for correct operation of the equipment, suitable flexible mountings may be used between the subframe and the chassis. Brackets should not be welded to the chassis frame and holes should not be drilled or punched in the top or bottom flanges of the chassis frame. The brackets should be attached to the frame web with fitted bolts with lock nuts or nuts and spring washers and, wherever possible, existing frame holes should be used.

It is essential that the maximum permitted axle loadings are not exceeded and that the transverse weight of the complete mounted unit is equally distributed on the chassis frame. Any side-to-side static load difference (in addition to the dynamic transfer of load when the drum is rotating) may result in permanent chassis twist and suspension sagging. To compensate for the transverse dynamic loading due to drum rotation, asymmetrical suspension may be required. Where the drum drive is to be taken from the gearbox, the maximum permissible torque output must not be exceeded. Similarly, front-mounted PTO torque limitations must be observed when installing hydraulic pumps.

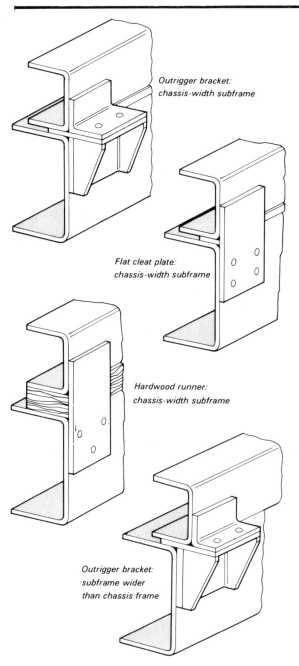

Outrigger bracket:
chassis-width subframe

Flat cleat plate:
chassis-width subframe

Hardwood runner:
chassis-width subframe

Outrigger bracket:
subframe wider
than chassis frame

Truck-mounted crane

Generally, truck-mounted cranes are hydraulically operated with a PTO/pump driven off the chassis gearbox and usually they are mounted directly behind the cab. This type of unit should be mounted on a continuous subframe extending from the front of the crane to the rear of the body or fifth wheel and attached to the chassis. The body subframe should be securely attached to the crane subframe to ensure continuity of section. Jack legs on outriggers attached to the subframe should be fitted to stabilize the vehicle and reduce the load on the chassis components whilst the crane is in use. The additional weight of the crane must not overload the front axle, taking into account the driver, passenger and payload. This type of crane has a high centre of gravity and weight transfer during braking on unladen vehicles and on especially short wheelbase units could cause the rear wheels to lock. The result is an unstable and possibly dangerous condition unless a brake load apportioning valve, specially adjusted to suit the requirements, is fitted.

Figure 117 *Subframe mountings*

11 Demountables

General principles

Demountable rigid trucks, drawbar trailers and semi-trailers with built on, self-motivated body-exchanging facilities are probably the most important distribution and cost-reducing development in commercial road transport since articulated vehicles came on the scene. Like the artic, the demountable leaves its cargo-carrying components behind for loading whilst the prime mover component (chassis cab) continues with other preloaded cargo units. However, the artic leaves behind sophisticated and expensive trailers, but the demountable leaves only a simple and relatively low-cost body unit to stand on legs, so a much higher proportion of the capital equipment achieves maximum utilization.

The demountable applies the practical application of the articulated principle to all size and weight categories of truck, drawbar trailer and

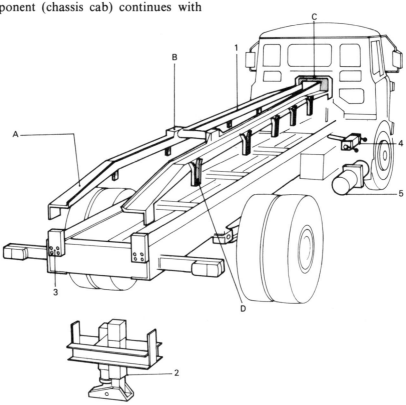

Figure 118   *Typical chassis installation for demountable body (see text for key)*

semi-trailer and in the process improves on most of the advantages of artics over conventional rigids.

Many transport and distribution managements use demountable systems as an integral part of their total distribution organization to confine and reduce distribution costs and improve management control of the transportation segment of distribution.

The cost savings and improved management controls can be substantial: fuel, chassis, bodies, wages, damage, stores and depots, insurance, rates, running costs and improved management controls over inflation, service, deliveries, loading congestion, overtime, security, driver and vehicle maintenance, driver and vehicle down time, seasonal trends, maintenance and service.

To increase the flexibility and the versatility of demountable systems and introduce additional combined materials-handling savings, an integral range of modular demountable systems have been designed and developed to work in conjunction with the standard systems or to operate independently, thus providing a most versatile combined cost-reducing range of demountables.

A typical chassis installation is shown in Figure 118. This is suitable for operations up to 15 tonnes GVW and has been designed and jig-constructed as a standardized self-contained assembly operating with a body base frame unit. Operation is either electrohydraulic or by PTO. The installation has the following characteristics:

1 Self-supporting beam, lipped chassis guide rail assembly incorporating:
   Demounted body unit pick up and alignment ramps (A).
   Fail-safe body unit cross-lock (B).
   Automatic front body unit locking and engine/cab protection assembly (C).
   Even load transmission and chassis flexibility brackets (D).
2 Hydraulic pivot ram assembly – mounted to the underside of the chassis.
3 Fail-safe misoperation body stop.
4 Control levers for hydraulic cross-lock and pivot ram, actuated by fail-safe 'dead man' push-button control.

5 Electrohydraulic power pack – used nationally for tail lifts.

Demountable performance

Every chassis manufacturer's equipment-mounting recommendations states:

'Equipment must avoid any concentration of stress on the chassis which can cause chassis and component failures and must transmit loads evenly to maintain chassis frame flexibility.'

Versatility Single, multiple and variations in body length operation on identical or mixed chassis are governed by the number of separation rams and body-locking mechanisms, their locations and the constraints imposed upon these mechanisms by variations in chassis frame widths, wheelbase settings and chassis component layouts.

Spring deflection Spring deflection is critical and governs cross-operation between all makes of demountable systems and demounted body unit heights.

Base frame deflection All methods of demounting and remounting body units subject base frames to deflection stresses. Excessive deflection leads to bowing and metal fatigue, reducing equipment life.

A complete base frame assembly is shown in Figure 119.

Demountable base frames have to be specifically designed and jig-constructed to:

1 Confine mounting and demounting deflection to a minimum over the length of the base frame under maximum load.
2 Maintain chassis unit flexibility.
3 Transmit loads evenly through the sub-assembly to the chassis frame.
4 Provide equivalent strength to the payload in the demounted position as the chassis frame.
5 Support the load in the demounted position in the safest known engineering method – with legs under compression.

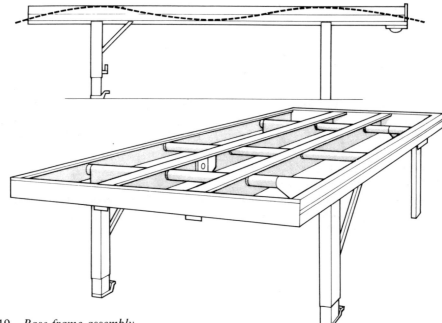

Figure 119   *Base frame assembly*

6   Occupy only the same loading space as conventional body units.
7   Be specifically designed to simplify the installation of any body unit specification.

Uneven load and operating surfaces (Figure 120)

Uneven load and rough, uneven operating surfaces can affect the stability of the demountable

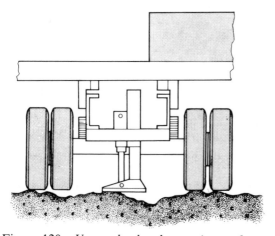

Figure 120   *Uneven load and operating surface*

unit and on occasions can prevent exchange facilities when body units are directly lifted off the chassis.

Control of misuse

All demountable systems are open to misuse: operation of separation ram with one or more body locks engaged, failure to apply all body locks for transit and misalignment of chassis withdrawal and re-entry.

Equipment life

The life and maintenance costs of all demountable equipment are directly related to the method of operation and the stress factors imposed on separation rams, leg members, base frames, body locks, chassis installations and the design strength and quality of engineering built in to each component.

Design concept and fundamentals

The fundamental purpose of any demountable system is to raise the vehicle body component sufficiently to allow lowering or positioning of the support legs upon which the body unit stands throughout the loading process whilst the freed chassis cab unit continues working with other. preloaded body units. Theoretically, the mechanical operation appears simple. It is comparatively easy to raise the body unit off the chassis member by using hydraulic rams or airbags mounted on the chassis, or with manual jacks operating between the ground and the body unit. It is also comparatively simple to construct a body unit either to incorporate a set of four legs or receive leg members to stand on in the demounted position.

Demountable systems provide operators with a number of design and construction benefits which both extend the applications of the demountable systems through integrated interchangeability and reduce operating and maintenance costs to those comparable with conventional rigids, whilst extending cargo-unit body life.

Body lifting system (Figure 121)

The simplest and safest known method of lifting a load is by applying the beam and fulcrum principle. All other methods of lifting are adaptations of this basic principle. Applied to demountables, this means using the chassis members as the beam and the front axle as the fulcrum, applying the actual movement of the lifting force to the rear of the chassis.

Demountable systems use this basic engineering principle, providing operators with the benefits of body unit and payload being supported by the combined lateral and longitudinal strength of the chassis members during key lifting and lowering

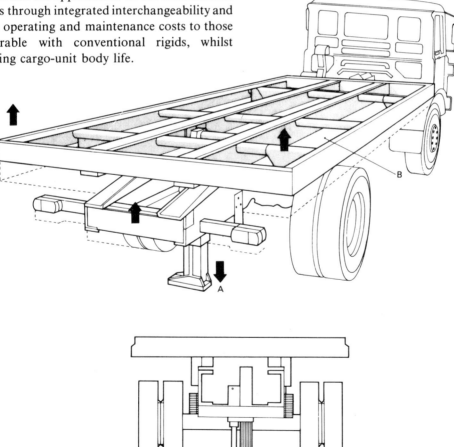

Figure 121   *Body lifting system*

operations and also confining the actual movement of lift to some 65 mm.

By pivoting the chassis on the front wheels with a lift ram using the ground as a base of the lifting torce (A), the body unit is supported through the lifting and lowering movements by the full length and lateral strength of the chassis frame and sub-assembly (B). This method of operation is the only known demountable system to comply specifically with the chassis manufacturers' recommendation to avoid concentrations of lift ram stress on chassis members.

The use of manual and hydraulic jacks, rams or airbags mounted on the chassis to separate the body unit can subject either the lifting mechanism, chassis or body unit to stresses which over a period of time can lead to an increase in maintenance costs.

Demounted body support system

The simplest and safest known method of supporting a load is by positioning the load on a base constructed to transmit the weight to a support directly under the load where it suffers purely compression force. Applied to demountables, this means using body units constructed to spread the load over the whole area of the floor, through to integral leg members working under compression.

The use of this basic engineering principle provides operators with the benefit of a body which is specifically constructed to spread uneven movements, loads and pressures over the whole area of the floor, the body unit being supported by leg members operating in the most beneficial manner, under compression.

Extended body life

Demountable operations subject the body units during lifting and lowering processes to deflection stresses, whichever method of mounting or demounting is employed. Excessive deflection, over a period of time, leads to metal fatigue and collapse and is preceded by bowing, which in the case of van bodies, racks or crimps their super-structure with consequential load damage.

Demountable bodies must be designed to confine longitudinal deflection within an acceptable engineering tolerance.

Maintenance

Since the primary virtue of demountables is that they reduce distribution costs it is essential that the inherent economies of the demountable principle are not eroded by the cost of maintaining them. For this reason, demountable equipment must be kept as mechanically simple as possible and be capable of fast servicing by ordinary, competent, commercial-vehicle maintenance crews. If this is achieved, then, on rigid chassis demountables, the maintenance commitment imposed by the demountable equipment can be discounted, as it is balanced by the improved accessibility of the bare, bodyless chassis.

Compared with articulated vehicles, demountables show substantial maintenance savings, the artic's semi-trailer requiring the servicing and replacement of additional road wheels, tyres, suspension, brake systems, lighting systems, etc.

Operating features

The success or failure of any demountable transport system is dependent upon the driver's ability to carry out the salient mounting and demounting operations single-handed, under the worst possible mental and climatic conditions, e.g. when he is tired and irritable, at night on mud or ice.

The demountable system is specifically designed to facilitate driver-only, all-condition operation and incorporates special features to enable it to be operated by a driver of no more than average intelligence and ability (classified Class 3 driver) and without his requiring special training. These features include:

1   Design of the chassis-mounted body pick-up guide rails provides for considerable misalignment of chassis and body during the pick-up manueovre.
2   The pick-up technique is such that the weight of the body and load is transferred to the

chassis before the rail of the chassis gets between the body's rear support legs. This ensures that there is maximum traction on the rear wheels and, therefore, minimum risk of skidding and chassis/leg contact during this critical manoeuvre.

3 Engagement of the front body securing hooks is automatic, relieving the driver of responsibility for initial body locking.

4 Engagement of the hydraulic cross-lock with its built-in safety mechanism is designed to reduce operation to two simple movements, the lifting of the control lever and activating of the push-button control to ensure driver participation.

5 The system can incorporate a fixed, stand-up rear end safety stop, manually operated safety stop, or a cab-operated safety stop to make demounting with the legs raised impossible.

6 Rear legs cater for varying ground levels through a simple telescopic height adjustment.

7 All controls are mounted on the off-side of the chassis and are clearly annotated for instant recognition. The design and position of the controls is ergonomically planned to reduce the number of physical operations by the driver to ensure his maximum participation.

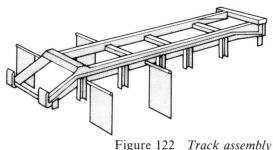

Figure 122 *Track assembly*

Assemblies

Track

The standard width track assembly (Figure 122) is mounted parallel to and above the chassis frame on equally spaced brackets rivetted to the vertical face of the chassis beams. This arrangement:

1 Transmits the loads evenly and maintains normal chassis flexibility.

2 Eliminates the necessity for positioning rams and body locks to suit variations in wheelbase settings and component layouts incurred in mixed-fleet chassis applications.

3 Locks the body unit to the chassis in the safest and strongest position between the frame members.

4 Standardizes components and simplifies installation and transfer of equipment.

5 Standardizes cross-lock operation in similar length and height chassis.

6 Provides long application life on more than one chassis.

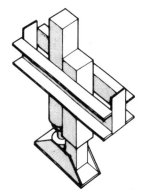

Figure 123 *Pivot ram assembly*

Pivot ram

The electrohydraulic or PTO ram assembly (Figure 123) is mounted behind the axle onto the underside of the chassis frame. This

1 Avoids any concentration of pivot ram stress on the chassis by using the ground as the base for the lift force.

2 Prevents chassis body and locking mechanism damage through the inability to demount with the bodylock engaged.

3 Provides maximum body unit mounting and demounting stability.

4 Simplifies installation and ease of transfer to next chassis.

5 Simplifies fitting to a drawbar or semi-trailer operation.

Base frame chassis locking (Figure 124)

Demountable base frame (A) chassis-locking mechanisms are designed to lock the base frame centrally, within the combined strength of the chassis frame members. Mounting and demounting rollers (B), built into the front of the base frame and housed in a box assembly, guide the base frame up the mounting ramps, along the lipped guide and body support rail and down the front ramp so that the locking housings in the front of the roller boxes (C) automatically locate with locking hooks built into the front body unit locking mechanism (D). The design of the front locking mechanism prevents any lateral or vertical movement of the base frame and body unit.

A fail-safe electrohydraulic cross-lock (E) mounted to the chassis assembly locks the demountable baseframe within the main chassis members, by projecting two tapered male cones into female recess housings, built into the main support longitudinal I beam members of the base frame. The combined action of the tapered cross-lock cones (E), the lipped track assembly (F), and the automatic front locks, both lock the base frame firmly to the chassis installation and clamp it down on to the support beams, preventing empty body clatter and wear.

Mounting and demounting

Mounting is simple, quick and fully controlled to prevent chassis, body unit and body-locking mechanism damage through mis-use. Body alignment is controlled throughout the mounting movements by the lipped chassis guide rail assembly. The mounting procedure is as follows:

Stage 1   The driver backs the chassis installation to visually locate the body unit mounting rollers on the chassis pick-up and alignment ramps.

Stage 2   The chassis is backed under the front of tne body unit up to the body-locking mechanism, the mounting rollers guiding the body unit up the tapered ramp, raising the front of the body unit and leg members by 65 mm or so.

Stage 3   Having applied the handbrake, the driver gets out and swings up the integrally mounted front legs, the weight of the leg being

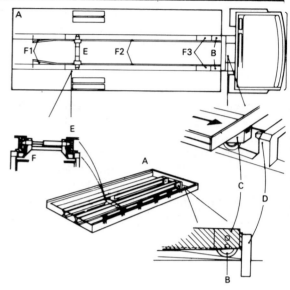

Figure 124   *Base frame chassis locking (see text for key)*

supported on the baseframe cross-tube member. A fail-safe misoperation body stop fitted to the rear cross-member of the chassis prevents the driver accidentally drawing forward and dropping the body unit when the front legs are recessed.

Stage 4   The driver backs the chassis fully under the body unit, the rollers on the body base frame guiding the body unit along and down the front tapers into the front automatic body-locking unit.

Stage 5   Having applied the handbrake, the driver gets out to lower the pivot ram unit. With the control lever in raise, the driver presses the push-button control and pivots the member on the front wheels raising the chassis to pick up the body unit supported by the full length chassis installation subframe.

Stage 6   With the body unit supported by the raised full-length chassis frame, the driver raises the rear leg members.

Stage 7   With the rear legs in position, the driver raises the pivot ram and is ready for transit.

To demount, the above operations are carried out in reverse order.

12 GRP/composite bodywork

Composite panelling

There is a wide range of composite panelling (see Figure 125) available to suit every type of body-building programme (dry freight panels, insulated panels, laminated flooring, etc.), manufactured under proprietory names.

General descriptions

Polyfont Smooth, brilliant white composite GRP/plywood panelling in a range of thicknesses and lengths.

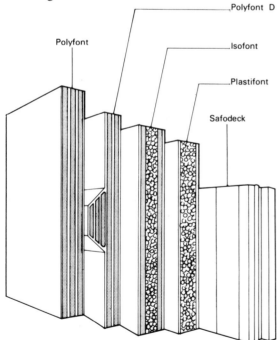

Figure 125 *Examples of composite body building panel*

Polyfont D Smooth, brilliant white composite GRP/plywood panelling of lightweight construction with vertical interior battens giving added strength and a facility for lashing points.

Isofont Smooth, brilliant white insulated construction panelling composed of polyurethane foam core with outer faces of GRP/plywood. This type of panelling is available with special glass-fibre membranes giving a total bond between both panel surfaces.

Plastifont High mechanical strength and lightweight smooth brilliant white panelling. Composed of polyurethane foam core faced on both sides with GRP. Special glass-fibre membranes give a total bond between both panel surfaces.

Safodeck This is a kiln-dried laminated hardwood, high-quality flooring for durability and ease of laying.

Specifications for Polyfont

Superior panel strength is achieved during the manufacturing process by subjecting the panel whilst in the press to heat, pressure and vacuum, thus ensuring the polyester resin is incorporated in the cellular structure of the plywood, giving tremendous strength to the bonding.

The composition of Polyfont is as follows:

Exterior surface Smooth brilliant white polyester resin reinforced with 300 or 450 g/m^2 of chop strand glass-fibre (CSGF) mat.

Board Exterior grade plywood made according to British Standards for WBP plywood.

Interior surface   Smooth matt white polyester-resin-reinforced with 300 or 450 g/m^2 of CSGF mat.

Thickness   Choice of standard range (8, 10, 12, 14, 17, 20 or 24 mm) depending on the size of vehicle and its purpose.

Size   Standard sizes varying from 2440 × 2440 mm (8 × 8 ft) to 12 200 × 2440 mm (40 × 8 ft).

Edges   All edges sealed with polyester.

Tolerance   On thickness ±0.5 mm, on size ±3 mm.

Odour   All panels comply with the relevant British Standards, i.e. less than 0.1% styrene.

Specifications for Polyfont D

The composition of Polyfont D is as follows:

Basic board   10 mm thick Polyfont panel.

Interior surface   Battens 20 mm deep mounted at 610-mm intervals and encapsulated in the final smooth white GRP.

Weight   Lightweight construction 10 kg/m^2; no extra support is needed for vehicle body-building.

Uses   All types of box vans, especially furniture vans. It can be used as an alternative interior face on Isofont insulated panels where air space is required.

Size   Up to 6100 × 2500 mm (28 ft × 8 ft 2½ in).

Specifications for Isofont

Exterior surface   GRP/plywood.

Insulation   Polyurethane foam, density 35 or 40 kg/m^2; self-extinguishing.

Interior surface   GRP/plywood, GRP/plywood with external battens (Polyfont D), pure GRP, stainless steel (Polynox), or aluminium.

Size   Panels available up to 12 200 × 2440 mm (40 × 8 ft).

Design   Every Isofont panel is manufactured to the customer's requirements. Vertical and horizontal inserts can be included in the panel for storage fixings and to accommodate fridge units.

Specifications for Plastifont

Composition   GRP outer layer/polyurethane foam/GRP inner layer.

Overall thickness   20 or 30 mm.

Construction   As extra support, wooden inserts are placed inside the panels at intervals of 1200 mm and around the perimeter. Lightweight, 8 kg/m^2. Has the same mechanical resistance as 17-mm thick Polyfont panel. No extra support needed for panel in body construction.

Size   12 200 × 2400 mm (40 × 8 ft) and 6100 × 2440 mm (20 × 8 ft).

Specifications for Safodeck

Safodeck consists of kiln-dried Malaysian hardwoods of prime quality and free from defects and splits. Components are not more than 32 mm wide nor less than 305 mm long. The average length is 915 mm or more. No end joints in adjacent components or two rows apart are less than 76 mm in between and no three joints in adjacent components are permitted in step fashion. Standard width is 305 mm in lengths of 6100 or 12 200 mm. Safodeck is overlapped with crush bead to eliminate warping.

Snap-Lok cargo van construction

The cargo van Snap-Lok unit is a glass-fibre-reinforced plywood body supplied and delivered to the customer as a construction set in kit form.

The assembly of the different components is made by simply engaging the appropriate Snap-Lok connector extrusions and pressing them together until they snap home. This system results in a simple and easy assembly procedure and provides clean wipe-down surfaces with no interior pillars to obstruct the interior of the unit.

The rear frame construction is of steel, with a section used for the corner posts to give maximum rigidity together with maximum rear door opening. Alternatively, a steel rear frame suitable for narrow or wide lathe shutters can be used and modifications can be made to suit tail-lift applications.

The roof is of one-piece, mill-finish 0.96-mm aluminium sheet, prestressed over aluminium roof bows set at 406-mm intervals; 305-mm diameter sky-lights can be fitted if required. An alternative option is the cargo van fabricated roof using mill-finish 0.81-mm aluminium sheet, solid rivetted on 50.8-mm pitch to 'zed' section stiffeners on 610-mm pitch. This option allows for 610-mm wide roof lights to be fitted. Supplied to special order, customers can choose to have side doors, roller shutters and an aluminium pre-paint white front wall with steel bracing to take a reefer refrigeration unit. Side and rear doors can be supplied in glass-fibre-reinforced plywood or in pre-paint white aluminium construction but it is recommended that all rear doors supplied in GRP/plywood should be fitted with an external power-brace-type lock mechanism.

Floors in excess of 8 m in length are delivered in two-part configuration having a rebated overlap to facilitate joining. The standard top cover of the floors consists of 15-mm thick exterior-grade marine ply, the top surface of which is treated with phenol resin. If the bodybuilder intends to finish the floor with glass fibre or other similar materials then the floor should be reversed so that the phenol resin finish is underneath. This is because adhesion problems can be encountered when trying to bond glass fibre or other synthetic materials to the floor finish.

Where the customer envisages a heavy-duty application, i.e. fork trucks entering unit- or pedestrian-controlled palettes generating high point loadings, 21-mm plywood should be used.

Construction details (Figures 126–130)

The fibre-reinforced plywood panelled body is produced from a material of incredible flexural strength and durability. Because of its remarkable properties this material takes operational 'wear and tear' like no other van body of comparable weight and thickness.

Smooth seamless panels of plywood are constructed with a 'gelcoat' plus a glass-fibre mat on the outside and inside. With many advantages over conventional materials, these panels with

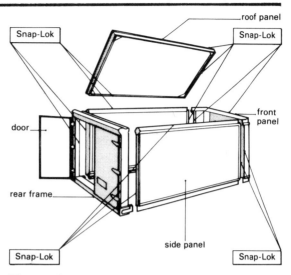

Figure 126   *General construction*

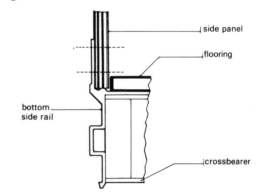

Figure 127   *Typical floor arrangement*

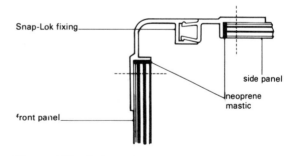

Figure 128   *Side to front arrangement*

their super-rigidity make them self-supporting.

The panel is finished with a hardened bottom and Snap-Lok top rail. Snap-Lok connector posts join the front wall and rear frame. The roof is also

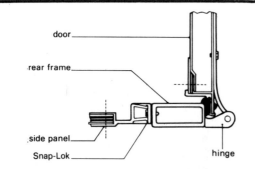

Figure 129   *Standard door arrangement*

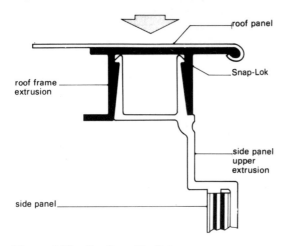

Figure 130   *Roof to side fixing*

of Snap-Lok construction to both side and front walls. No interior pillars obstruct the inside surface and valuable extra freight capacity is gained by using all of the internal width.

Almost maintenance-free, the cargo van has a long proven life and is remarkably scuff and impact resistant. The fabricated aluminium roof is available with full-width roof lights or alternatively, full glass-fibre one-piece sheet.

Fastening

Fastening is achieved by inserting a metal sleeve (see Figure 131) through the materials with the sleeve head giving a low profile on the inner lining. The design provides an uninterrupted projection- and snag-free surface to the interior of the van. Additionally it provides uniform clamping force,

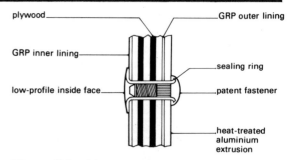

Figure 131   *Sleeve-type fastener*

high shear and tension strengths and is vibration resistant.

Advantages

Toughness   This lightweight laminated glass-fibre/plywood material is used for the cargo van because of its exceptional flexural strength, stiffness and durability. In operation it can take far more abuse and rough handling than most other materials available.

Hygiene   The exceptionally smooth walls (up to 12×2.5 m in a single sheet) of the GRP cargo van eliminates any chance of the build-up of dirt or bacteria. Such a feature allows the container to be easily and quickly hosed down or steam-cleaned.

Space saving   The construction of the GRP cargo van with its pillar-free interior design enables all of the space to be used for the cargo. This is achieved without sacrificing strength, rigidity or its modern protective qualities.

Smoothness   The cargo vans' completely smooth surfaces are weather- and rust-proof. Possible scuffing or damage to the cargo whilst loading or unloading is eliminated by its snag-free interior.

Glass-fibre skin   Produced by a special process, the skin is resistant to most acids and chemical contamination and maintains a high thermal efficiency.

Ease of repair   Very severe impact may result in damage to a surface; this can be quickly and cheaply rectified with a cargo van repair kit, thus reducing the job to a semi-skilled operation.

Aluminium extrusions/composite panels

The use of aluminium extrusions with composite panels combines the lightweight and high strength properties of aluminium with the advantages of GRP/ply to provide an easy-to-assemble, long-lasting vehicle body. The range of extrusions are designed to provide the bodybuilder with a choice of construction methods and can accommodate 8.5, 11.5, 14.5, 18 and 21 mm composite panels.

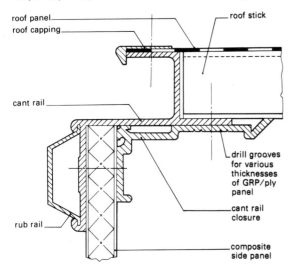

Figure 132 *One-piece full cant rail*

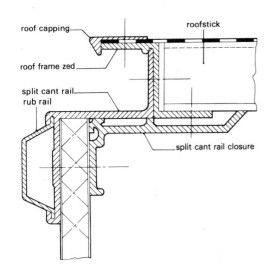

Figure 133 *Split cant rail*

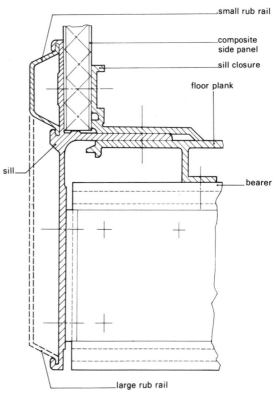

Figure 134 *Sill detail*

A choice of cantrails, either full or split, enables roof assembly on the body or as a separate component (see Figures 132 and 133).

Top corner castings are available to suit both cant rails with or without the top rub rail.

The design of the sill (see Figures 134 and 135) facilitates the use of either a 75- or a 101-mm cross-bearer with either an aluminium or timber floor. A choice of rub rails is also available to suit customers' requirements.

A typical corner arrangement (see Figure 136) as an alternative to Snap-Lok construction would comprise the front and side composite panelling sandwiched between an exterior pillar extrusion and an interior pillar closure extrusion.

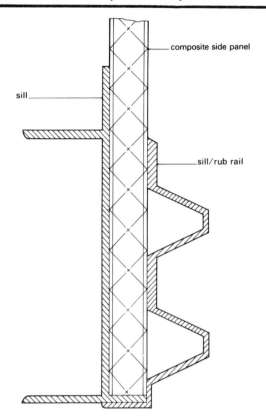

Figure 135   *Sill detail*

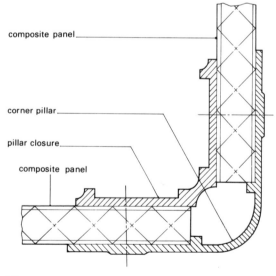

Figure 136   *Typical corner arrangement*

The Health and Safety at Work Act, 1974

General

GRP panels are supplied for use in the construction of reinforced plastic freight containers and commercial vehicles and as far as is possible to determine, all materials used in the construction of these panels make them suitable for this purpose. Where GRP composite panels are to be used in applications other than freight containers and commercial vehicles, e.g. building, furniture, toys, etc., care should be taken to ensure that the material complies with the necessary requirements and regulations.

Machining of panels

The handling of GRP composite panels presents no exceptional hazard to health but some risk to health could arise if the panels are machined since dust is produced. All such dust should be removed before the panels are used as part of a food-carrying container.

Workshop practice

If panels are to be machined, it is advisable that dust masks, goggles, gloves and other protective clothing should be worn and that good workshop practice be strictly enforced. Some people machining or handling freshly machined panels for the first time may experience skin irritation. This is usually of a temporary nature and can be minimized by wearing loose clothing and by avoiding tight constrictions round the neck, wrists, etc. The use of barrier creams is a matter of preference but skin irritation can be minimized by rinsing the skin under running water before applying soap when washing. The need for adequate standards of personal hygiene should be recommended. Employees who are known to have suffered from dermatitis, skin sensitization or asthma should not work on the machining or handling of freshly machined panels unless medical clearance has been obtained.

13 Timber and plywood in vehicle building

Timber bodywork

Timber. although replaced by metals for body main framing purposes, is still widely used for the floors of platform trucks and vans, for the construction of livestock carriers and on vehicles on which the traditional craftsmanship is of prestige value.

For flooring, the structural properties of wood are relatively unimportant, the desired qualities being straight grain, freedom from knots and good dimensional stability. Cheapness is the main requirement and this generally limits the choice to imported softwoods such as Columbian pine (Douglas fir) and the Baltic whitewoods, though Scottish-grown larch is in limited use.

Where very heavy wear is encountered (as in cattle trucks, or vehicles for carrying heavy machinery), imported hardwoods such as keruing and yang are tending to replace the elm floors traditionally used.

Small blocks of hardwood and pieces of ply are used in vehicle building either for providing fixings in the body structure or where complex shapes are more costly or more difficult to achieve in metals.

Hardwoods generally used include ash, oak, red niangon and teak and, except where glueing is involved, these are treated with a wood preservative before installation. For conveyance of foodstuffs, a check should be made on the toxicity of the preservative.

Timber should be selected with care, being preferably air-seasoned with a moisture content of between 15 and 20% and reasonably free from warps, checks, splits and shakes.

Timber splicing

One of the most common forms of joint in use in timber framing both for new work or repair is the scarf joint. There are several forms of scarf joint, the simplest of all being the sawn bevel (Figure 137) with the two mating surfaces of the joint butted together, glued and screwed or painted and screwed.

Figure 137   *Sawn bevel*
Figure 138   *Half-joint splice*
Figure 139   *End bevel half-joint splice*
Figure 140   *Bevelled splice joint*

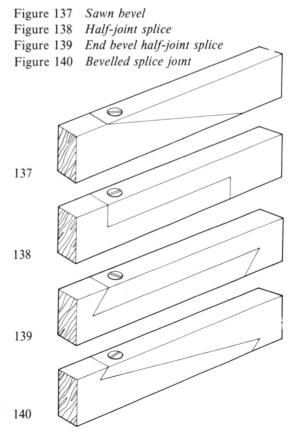

137

138

139

140

The half-joint splice (Figure 138) is better but still not particularly strong. This joint would tend to split from the corners along the joint grain; in addition it could quite easily open out if any stress were applied to the face.

The end-bevelled half-joint (Figure 139) is a much stronger splice which cannot open at the face but it may split from the joint corners.

By far the strongest joint of the splice type is the bevelled scarf (Figure 140) with both ends also bevelled. This joint when made correctly will really lock together. It will not come apart from face stress due to the end bevels and there is far less tendency for it to split along the grain. In addition, when the joint is screwed together, the wood screws pass through the thin wood into the thick resulting in a more secure joint as the screws are far less likely to shear off.

In the case of timber framing, any fractures will most likely be from a joint as this is the weakest part of any framing other than defective timber. It is quite common to find that a split has occurred from a half-joint either on a skirt rail to pillar joint or on a pillar to bottom side joint. Ideally, such damaged members should be removed and replaced with a completely new section, but this would involve considerable time, therefore splicing may be used to reduce the repair time.

The effects of force on a joint

1 Tension tends to pull the joint apart in a direct line at right-angles to the joined faces. Drawer fronts are in tension while the drawer is being pulled.
2 Torsion is a tendency to twist. Stiles to which doors are hinged are in torsion.
3 Shear is a force applied along the line of a joint. Rails supporting drawers are in shear.
4 Cleavage due to modified shear is a tendency to pull out of square.
5 Compression holds the joints together.
6 Many joints are designed to withstand more than one force but some rely on the support of cladding, other rails or adjoining bulkheads to hold them true.

The factors that may influence the selection of a particular joint are as follows:

a Whether the joint is load-bearing or not.
b Whether the joint is heavily stressed.
c Whether the joint is in tension, torsion, cleavage, shear or compression.
d Whether the joint will be completely concealed or not.
e Whether appearance is important on one side only or on two or more sides.
f Whether it matters if the end grain of the timber shows or not.

Making joints from pre-cut timber

Nearly all of the timber used for making up a vehicle body is machined ready for assembly in the body shop. The essential points and procedure are as follows:

1 Check each joint for fit.
2 Reject all timber which is a loose fit.
3 Ease all joints which are too tight, taking surplus wood from the least loaded member.
4 Ensure that important dimensions are not altered, e.g. position of window or door pillars. Keep outer surfaces flush for panelling.
5 Drill for screws with a clearance drill and countersink – in hardwoods, use a pilot drill for the screw threads.
6 Paint the mating surfaces of the joints; this seals the grain, acts as a lubricant for the joints and lessens the chances of 'squeaking'.
7 Fit the joint, check for alignment (squareness), clamp and screw the parts together.
8 Check that no splits have occurred and that the joint surfaces lie flush where necessary.

Joints are seldom glued as this makes the body members difficult to replace and produces a joint that squeaks badly when aged and flexible.

Glue-laminating

The process of 'glue-laminating' consists of the fabrication of straight or bent wood members built up of thin sections bonded into one rigid piece with glue. The grain in all the plies is parallel in contrast to plywood panels.

In order to make up any lamination length required, glued bevel scarf joints are used. Curved members are produced by bending the laminations to shape by hand or by mechanical means in a suitable jig during assembly and then cramping all laminations together for the required adhesive curing time.

As curving of laminations produces pre-stress in each lamination, it is desirable that the radii of curvature should be limited according to the species of timber and thickness of laminae. Allowable working stresses in glued laminated components can generally be considered to be about 30% above those of solid timber due to the better disposition of the fault characteristics of timber by dispersal among the various laminations.

Precautions necessary to the successful production of glue-laminate members are:

1 All laminae should be perfectly clean and free from any substance liable to affect glue-curing.
2 The moisture content of the laminae should be between 12 and 15%.
3 The timber should be kept in a temperature of not less than 15°C and a relative humidity of between 55 and 65% for 24 hours before gluing.
4 The cramping pressure should be sufficient to maintain laminations in intimate contact and ensure that the adhesive forms a continuous film of even thickness through the whole cramping time. Glue-laminating is economical where at least six identical members are required from one jig. The practical aspects of making up curved members, or employing smaller cross-sections of equivalent strength to a solid section, or for providing very stable components not subject to warping or twisting, are some of its advantages.

Timber preservation

This means treating timber with solutions poisonous to fungi, insects and marine borers. It also enables non-durable timbers to be placed in a higher category.

Timber may decay given the following conditions:

a High moisture content.
b Lack of ventilation.
c A timber of low natural durability used in situations where (a) and (b) exist.

This can be prevented:

1 By using timbers of high natural durability.
2 By applying a suitable wood preservative.

Classification of wood preservatives

Class TO – Tar-oil type:
TO1   Coal tar creosote to BS 144.
TO2   Coal tar oil types

Class OS – Organic solvents type:
OS1   Chloronapthalenes
OS2   Metallic napthalenes
OS3   Pentachlorophenol (BWPA standards)

Class WB – Water-borne types:
WB1   Copper/chrome
WB2   Copper/chrome/arsenate
WB3   Fluoride/arsenate/chromate
WB4   Sodium fluoride
WB5   Boron compounds

Methods of application

Pressure Timber is placed in a metal container and the preservative forced into the timber under pressure. This method permits control of the amount of wood preservative absorbed.

Hot and cold treatment Timber is placed in a tank of wood preservative which is heated. The timber is then kept in the preservative while it cools or placed in a tank of cold preservative.

Cold-dipping and steeping Timber is immersed in cold preservative; the longer the period, the more effective the treatment, particularly with tar oils.

Brushing and spraying Gives surface protection only.

Table 5 *Use of various timber preservative treatments*

Treatment	Application	Type of preservative
Pressure	Most timbers and the sapwood of all timbers	TO1, OS3, WB1,2,3
Hot and cold open tank treatment	Permeable timbers and the sapwood of all timbers	TO1,2 OS2,3 WB2,3
Cold dipping and steeping	Permeable timbers and sapwood of all timbers	TO1,2 OS1,2,3 WB4
Brushing and spraying	Particularly suitable for timbers *in situ*. Not normally used if deep penetration is necessary	TO1,2 OS1,2,3 WB1
Diffusion	Softwood timbers not exceeding 75 mm in thickness used under protection of roof and/or the surface sealed by the application of a coating such as oil-based paint. It is not intended for use where there is direct contact with the ground or where continuous wet conditions are involved	WB5

Diffusion This is mainly carried out at the sawmill with timber freshly felled and milled. The timber is completely immersed in the preservative and then close-piled to allow diffusion through the wood.

The use of the various treatments is tabulated in Table 5 and the amount of penetration of wood preservatives using these methods is shown diagrammatically in Figure 141.

Plywood applications

'Plywood' may be defined as a 'number of thin layers of wood, each being of a definite thickness, glued together with the grain of the adjacent layers

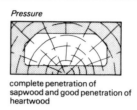

complete penetration of sapwood and good penetration of heartwood

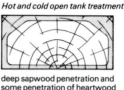

Hot and cold open tank treatment

deep sapwood penetration and some penetration of heartwood

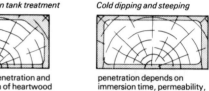

Cold dipping and steeping

penetration depends on immersion time, permeability, moisture content and type of preservative

Brushing and spraying

surface protection with variable penetration into sapwood

Diffusion

almost complete penetration

Figure 141 *Timber preservation: penetration of wood preservatives using different methods*

at right-angles to each other'. The main sources of the base timber are the Baltic states, Canada and Africa, most of the 'exterior' grade plywoods being of birch, Columbian pine or one of the many African hardwoods.

All exterior plywoods are bonded with exterior phenolic resin adhesive. The adhesive complies with British Standard 1203:1963 which reads 'Type WBP – weather- and boil-proof adhesives that by systematic tests and by their records in service over many years have been proved to make joints highly resistant to weather, micro organisms, cold and boiling water, steam and dry heat'.

For permanently high moisture conditions (moisture content above 20%), plywood can be supplied, preservative-treated, to give complete protection against fungal and insect attack.

Plywoods combine light weight with well-defined two-way strength properties and because of these properties plywood panels are well-known among vehicle builders for use as lorry and trailer floors, as well as for sides, linings and doors in all types of vehicles. Panels are also used in box vans for strengthening timber frameworks.

When machined or overlaid with a range of industrial surfaces, plywood panels have additional advantages. For example, floors cut exactly to the size required for the vehicle save time and labour in assembly.

The range of surfaces available allows the most economic and appropriate plywood to be chosen. Embossed rubber or resin-surfaced panels can be used for non-slip floors, tough GRP-surfaced panels for heavy-duty lorry decks and aluminium-surfaced panels for sidewalls or doors. Resin-impregnated paper-faced plywood has been specially developed to give high quality paint finishes and is ideal for vehicle sides that are to be signwritten. For food-carrying vehicles, taint-free finishes of GRP, polyester and painted surfaces are available.

Structural plywoods make excellent decks for trailers and other commercial vehicles.

Compared with solid timber, these plywoods have extremely high static and impact strength and are highly resistant to abrasion. They are also very stable and will not shrink. In exceptionally severe conditions, specially coated plywoods can be used to provide, for example, increased surface life and non-skid decks. Compared with timber boards for flooring, plywood panels are simply fixed and are therefore easy both to assemble and repair. When large production runs are required, whole floors can be supplied in one or more panels machined and drilled to the vehicle manufacturer's precise requirements.

Reinforcement of timber outriggers (Figure 142)

Timber outriggers are prone to failure where they cross the longitudinal chassis member. They can be simply reinforced by plywood doubling plates. Comparatively thin plywood plates, glued and screwed in position, will considerably increase both the static and impact strength of the cross-member (a structural adhesive must be used).

Alternative floor rave constructions used with plywood decks (see Figure 143) are:

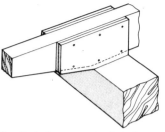

Figure 142   *Reinforcement of timber outriggers*

a A square timber side rave with a flat steel angle capping. The plywood floor is butted to the steel angle. This is a single assembly giving easy access for repairs or renewals. The joints must be well sealed on assembly to prevent any water seepage.

b A square timber side rave rebated to accept the plywood floor. The side rave is topped with a flat steel capping. This is a standard form of construction and gives improved protection to the plywood edge against water seepage.

c A bevelled timber side rave with a rebate for the floor and fitted with a nosed capping. This construction is of particular benefit where side loading is regularly used.

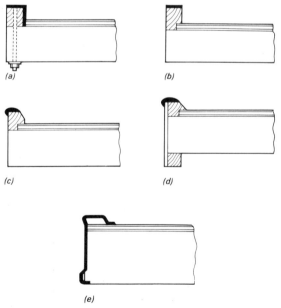

Figure 143   *Floor rave constructions (see text for key)*

d A deep-sided rave, rebated for the plywood floor, with an iron nose capping. A plywood edge-board is incorporated as an outside finisher, masking all the edge finishes. Where signwriting is required along the rave, this construction is of particular value. The outside finisher should be painted on all faces and edges to protect it from weathering.

e A typical use of an alloy side rave section with a plywood floor. The section gives full protection to the floor edges and cross-bearers. There are several light-alloy rave sections available.

Dropsides and tailboards

Timber framed The good screw-holding and bolt-holding of birch plywood together with its high impact strength means that a minimum of fixings need to be employed. Edges of the plywood should be sealed before assembly into the framing and any butt joints in the ply should occur on the framing members. The life of the dropside can be prolonged by treating the timber and plywood with a non-leaching preservative.

Metal-framed The plywood panel fits into a light-alloy extruded section. The plywood panel including its edges should be pre-painted with sealant before assembling to the light-alloy section and drain holes should be drilled in the aluminium framing at intervals.

Wheel-arches

Square wheel-arches can be manufactured easily and quickly with a minimum of wastage. The strong flexural stiffness of the birch plywood panels means that a minimum of framing members are required.

Thinner birch plywood is readily curved without heat or stress, particularly across the face grain. When curved, it has considerably higher strength than a flat panel of the same thickness.

Plywood can be used to reinforce a timber wheel-arch frame, the strength being considerably increased without appreciable weight increase. These components can usually be made from

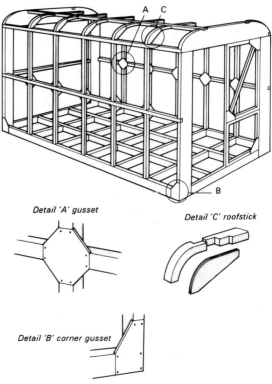

Figure 144   *Timber box van reinforcement*

spare offcuts. Timbers and plywoods used in wheel-arch constructions and linings should be preservative-treated to give maximum useful life. An additional protection from the action of salt/sand mixtures can be gained by covering the exposed area with glass-reinforced polyester resin.

Reinforcement of timber box van framing

The method is shown in Figure 144.

Detail 'A' gusset Plywood gussets let into the main frame timbers will considerably increase the strength of the joint and its resistance to vibration. Normally the gusset would be glued and screwed to the main framing members using a structural adhesive.

Detail 'B' corner gusset Where corner gussets are used with standing pillars it is advisable to use thicker plywood than for ordinary gussets.

Detail 'C' roofstick When roofsticks are cut from the solid, strength will be progressively reduced on the curve as the cross-grain is met. By rebating back and introducing a similar shaped piece of plywood on one or both sides of the stick, greater strength and rigidity is gained at the joint, whilst still giving the degree of flexibility necessary in van bodywork construction. The detail shown is a typical method of roofstick reinforcement.

Box van panelling and cladding

The various panels are shown in Figure 145. Specifications for these are as follows:

Sides, front and rear headboards Exterior quality plywood or preservative-treated exterior plywood:

Standard panels or full-sized sheets.
Typical thickness: 9 mm on framing at 609.6 mm (24 in) centres.
Panel surface – outside face: unsurfaced plywood, pre-surfaced for painting, phenol or melamine self-coloured films, or chopped strand or woven roving glass-fibre faced panels.
Panel surface – inside face: unsurfaced plywood, or phenol or melamine self-coloured films.

Floors Exterior quality plywood or preservative-treated exterior plywood:

Standard panels or full-sized sheets.
Thickness: lightweight, 9-12 mm; medium duty, 15-18 mm; heavy duty, 21-24-27 mm.
Panel surface – top side: unsurfaced plywood, phenol coated or glass-fibre surface, all with or without non-skid patterning.
Panel surface – underside: unsurfaced plywood or phenol self-coloured.

Half or full linings Exterior quality plywood. This should be preservative-treated only if plywood lining is unpainted and condensation or extreme wetting can occur.

Standard panels or full-size panels. Smaller panels can be supplied cut to exact size.

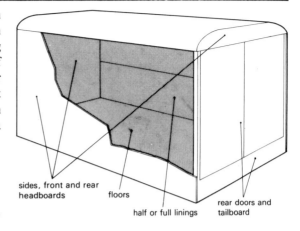

sides, front and rear headboards   floors   half or full linings   rear doors and tailboard

Figure 145 *Box van pannelling and cladding*

Typical thickness: 6.5 mm on framing at 609.6 mm (24 in) centres.
Panel surfaces: unsurfaced plywood, or phenol or melamine self-coloured films.

Rear doors and tailboard Exterior quality plywood and preservative-treated exterior plywood cut from standard sizes or exact cut sizes to special order.

Typical thickness: 18 mm unframed.
Outside: unsurfaced plywood, pre-surfaced for painting, aluminium or steel faced, or glass-fibre coatings.
Inside: unsurfaced plywood, phenol coat or phenol self-coloured film, glass-fibre coatings, or aluminium or steel faced, all with or without non-skid patterns for tailboard.

Bus and coach applications

Plywood panels have long been used in bus and coach building for floors to which other surfacing materials were applied. Now non-slip panels are available which are hardwearing and require no further surfacing. Other functional and decorative pre-surfaced panels such as veneered, GRP and heavy-duty film-faced can be used for linings, kick-boards and luggage racks, again requiring no further surface treatment. In thinner sections, the plywood panels are used for curved linings and for seats, and backs for upholstery.

Caravans

The high strength of plywood panels enables them to be used in very thin sections for caravan bodywork, thus reducing weight. The thicker section panels provide strong, stiff floors.

The smooth sanded surface of the plywood itself provides a good base for painting. To achieve a top quality paint finish, paper-faced panels for painting should be used. The resin-impregnated paper film provides a smooth stable base and a good key for painting operations and the panels require no priming or other preparation.

Standard film-faced, decorative film-faced, pre-painted, decorative veneered, laminate-faced and GRP polyester-surfaced plywoods can be used for fitments and bodywork and non-slip surfaces are useful for floors and steps.

Railway goods wagons and passenger carriages

Goods wagons have to carry a wide variety of loads ranging from abrasive raw materials to heavy manufactured products. Heavy-duty film-faced panels, developed to withstand abrasion in loading and unloading, are employed as wagon sides. Tough GRP-surfaced and metal-surfaced panels give even longer life. Panels surfaced with phenol resin or phenolic film imprinted with mesh pattern or panels surfaced with patterned glass fibre are used for non-slip floors.

Decorative veneered, laminate-faced and coloured film-faced panels are economical pre-surfaced materials for passenger coach interior linings and fitments requiring no further surface treatment after assembly.

Freight containers

Many freight containers are constructed with floors of 24, 27 and 30 mm thick birch plywood panels, which give good service life thereby reducing repair costs to operators and lessors.

Floors can be supplied with smooth or non-slip surfaces and special veneer lay-ups are available for extra strength. Several types of GRP surfaces are available for one-piece panel sides, roofs and ends for refrigerated and insulated containers and standard or metal-faced panels are used for doors. Plywood finds similar applications in small boat and shipbuilding.

Fasteners

Plywood panels are easily fixed together on to wood or metal framing by bolts, rivets or self-tapping screws, as well as the more traditional ways of connecting plywood to timber by nails, screws, staples or glue. The cross-banded construction makes it possible to position fasteners close to the edges of panels without the risk of break-out. In all joints where the plywood is exposed to moisture penetration, the edges of panels should be sealed or otherwise protected.

Rivets

Conventional riveting of plywood to vehicle body framing follows broadly the practice used for other materials, but a metal washer should always be included between the rivet and the plywood.

When driving in rivets, it is important that they should be knocked down with a minimum number of blows to prevent any local squeezing of the plies. Blind rivets are available for attaching plywood to plywood or plywood to metal; these are high-clench rivets for which no special clenching tools are required.

Holes and drill sizes follow those normally used, allowing the rivet to slide smoothly through the hole on assembly in order to prevent deformation of the joint during service life.

Rivet pitch for unstressed joints can be up to eighteen times the general thickness of the plywood. The minimum edge distance should be twice the rivet diameter. When joints are overlapped, the minimum overlap should be six times the rivet diameter. Rivets should never be driven into the end grain of plywood.

Bolts

When plywood panels are required to be removable, bolts should be used for the fixing. The use of washers under hexagon-head bolts and nuts is recommended in order to avoid crushing the plywood if over-tightening occurs.

When fixing thick plywood panels, e.g. floors, countersunk-headed bolts can be used. Alternatively, to obtain a smooth surface, hexagon-headed bolts can be sunk into a hole not deeper than half the thickness of the plywood and to a diameter large enough to accept a flat metal washer under the bolt head and sufficient clearance for a box spanner.

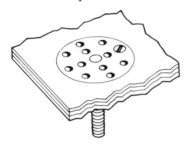

Figure 146 *'Big head' type bolt*

'Big head' bolts (Figure 146) which consist of a large perforated disc having a stud welded in the centre can be applied by passing the stud through the plywood and securing the plate in position with a small wood screw. Alternatively, it can be bonded into position with reinforced plastics. This type of bolt spreads the local loading over a larger area.

Woodworking

Much of the popularity of plywood is due to the relatively easy way in which cleanly machined edges can be achieved. Tungsten carbide tipped tools will give longest life before sharpening is required.

Circular sawing

Cutting with the face grain always gives a cleaner edge than cutting across the grain so the saw should be adjusted on a cross-grain cut. Counter sawing not climb sawing should be used. Counter sawing means that the teeth of the saw enter the plywood on the unsupported face side.

The plywood panel should be fed into the saw as quickly as possible, consistent with safe handling, and the panel should be well supported by the bench in the region of the saw blade. The saw depth should be set so that when cutting, the teeth just show above the top face of the panel.

Spindle moulding

The best results are achieved when spindle moulding by using a high cutter sharpness angle together with a high number of cuts per unit length. In contrast to sawing, the cleanest edges are obtained with fairly slow material feed.

Routing plywood

For general routing work, where a clean face is required to the panel, tests have shown that spoon cutters revolving at a fast cutting speed give the best results, especially if a slow material feed speed is used. If, however, for some reason the appearance of the edge of the plywood is more important than its face, then multi-wing cutters, revolving at a fast cutting speed with fast material feed speed should be used.

Drilling

Whenever possible, the drill should enter the plywood on its 'best' face where this is applicable. Backing the plywood with scrap material will help to give a clean break-out of the drill. Panels, particularly when cut down to small sizes, should be firmly clamped to a base plate during drilling to avoid pick-up. When drilling thicker plywoods a vertical drill stand should be used to ensure that the holes are square to the panel faces.

Gluing

The parts to be glued should be clean and free from grease and dust and the correct type of adhesive for the job (following manufacturer's instructions) should be used.

There is usually no advantage to be gained by roughing the surfaces to be joined before applying the adhesive. Generally the glue joint will be stronger if the members are held together under firm pressure until the glue cures. In glued joints exposed to weathering or excessive moisture, a resorcinal or phenol resorcinal type of adhesive should be used when bonding plywood to timber, or an epoxy type when bonding plywood to metal. For joints that are not fully exposed to excessive moisture a urea formaldehyde type of adhesive will be suitable for plywood to timber joints.

A wide variety of adhesives is available for bonding covering materials to plywood, dependent upon the material. It is advisable to obtain the glue manufacturer's recommendations with regard to the use of adhesives for particular purposes and their recommendations should be followed carefully.

Painting plywood

Plywoods with face veneers are particularly economical to paint with pleasing results. The smooth sanded faces give an excellent surface finish even with light or pastel paint shades. If the panels are dry and free of grease, almost every type of paint product can be applied successfully and easily.

The best results will be obtained if these general hints are followed:

1   In all cases the edges and backs of panels should be paint sealed against the possibility of moisture penetration. This is especially necessary when exterior plywood is to be exposed to wet or damp conditions over a prolonged period. Any re-cut edges of pre-surfaced boards should be re-sealed with a waterproof paint.
2   Best results will be obtained if paint is applied when the plywood has a low moisture content (10 to 14%). With the high humidity which generally prevails in the UK, panels can pick up moisture if stored for too long. Prolonged

storage of boards should be avoided by stock rotation.
3   Use good quality primers. Avoid the so-called pink primers, some of which are not durable enough for exterior applications.
4   All wood products move slightly with changes in temperature and humidity. To compensate for any movement that might affect the paint film, flexible paints should be used.

Alternatively, plywood can be supplied surfaced with a thin laminate specially developed for overpainting. This reinforces the paint film and gives a top quality result with the minimum of paint.

Pre-preservative-treated plywoods, i.e. plywoods which have been preservative-treated during the plywood manufacturing process, are easily painted in the usual way.

If the boards are treated after manufacture, it should be remembered that some organic solvent preservatives or water-repellent preservatives are not suitable for over-painting. If the plywood is to be painted, use only those preservatives which are stated by their manufacturers to be suitable for this purpose.

Method of application

All current methods of application can be used successfully. The flat smooth panels lend themselves particularly to continuous painting line production. The choice of method depends on the job required:

Spray gun   Manually operated spray guns either with cups or in conjunction with pressure pots may be used effectively. Nitrocellulose and polyurethane finishes are suited to this method.

Hot spray gun   Suitable for use with hot nitrocellulose solutions in order to achieve a higher build.

Airless spray   Valuable for on-site spraying where fume exhaust is not possible.

Dual feed equipment   This eliminates the need for prior mixing of two component materials.

Components are mixed in the air after ejection from the special spray gun and before alighting on the surface. It is especially useful for polyester application.

Roller coater Excellent for application of primers.

Reverse roller coater Especially useful for the application of heavy fillers.

Curtain coater In this continuous system, paint film thickness is easily controllable. Little turbulence is caused in the film and the method is therefore ideal for producing high quality surfaces.

Repairing damaged panels

Floors

If the damage is localized, a rectangular hole can be cut out to include the damaged area. The cut should finish on the centre-line of a cross-bearer. Alternatively, cut to the edge of the cross-bearer and support with a supplementary bearer which is screwed to the original. The plywood face grain of the patch must run across the bearers.

Body panels

Small local damage should be repaired by patches or a filler. Patches can be made from plywood and keyed in position by either cutting the patch on an angle or alternatively by using two thicknesses of plywood when the panel thickness permits it. With thin panels it may be necessary to use an inside cover plate.

The patch should be made first and used as a pattern for marking the panel over the damaged area. The patch should be fixed with exterior quality adhesive and wood screws. With very small areas of damage, particularly when the board is not penetrated, surface repairs can be carried out with a non-shrink weatherproof filler such as an epoxy filler. All damaged and loose plywood films should be removed and filler applied flush to the outer plywood surface. This should be smoothed off when dry and colour touched in to match the body panel.

Twill reinforcement

When plywood panels have suffered local damage, and repair rather than replacement is required, this can be effected by using a synthetic filler together with twill material as reinforcing.

Storage of materials

To get the best results from plywood panels they should be properly stored before use. They should always be protected from the weather by storing them under cover in a well-ventilated building. If the panels are held in store for a long period, say over three months, some form of gentle heating may be needed to keep the panels at the right dryness for processing.

Boards are best kept flat. Ideally they should be 'sticked' with batons of scrap timber to separate each board and allow the passage of air.

Pre-surfaced boards will not readily pick up moisture in storage because of their protective edge and face coatings, but in general these panels will also benefit from good storage.

Processed panels

Plywood panels can be surfaced and machined to provide defined properties. The different types of pre-surfaced panels manufactured are as follows:

Standard film-faced These plywood panels have a surface film of cellulose impregnated with a phenolic resin. All panels are edge-sealed against moisture uptake. Film-faced plywood panels have a number of useful properties including improved resistance to abrasion, moisture, chemicals, insects and fungi. The panels have a smooth hygienic, cleanable surface and are non-toxic. The colour is normally brown but panels can be obtained in green or yellow. A textured pattern can also be imprinted into the film overlay to give non-slip characteristics.

Heavy-duty film-faced A thick cellulose surface film, heavily impregnated with phenolic resin, is applied to the faces of the plywood panels giving even better surface properties than standard film-faced panels. The colour is dark brown.

Decorative plastic film   These plywood panels are available in several decorative colours. For interior use, a film is applied usually a polyvinyl resin type. For exterior use, the film is either polyester or polyvinyl chloride (PVC).

Prepainted   Plywood panels are supplied prepainted with a variety of primers and paints such as polyurethane and epoxy in various colours. In some instances, the surface may be paper-faced before the paint is applied to give a top quality paint finish with improved weathering characteristics. The paint systems can include aggregate to provide textured or non-slip characteristics.

Paper-faced for painting   Heavy-duty kraft paper, lightly impregnated with a synthetic resin for exterior painting, is bonded to the plywood panels. A lighter paper is used for panels intended for interior painting. These paper films provide a smooth stable base and a good key for painting operations and the panels require no priming or other preparation, thus saving labour and paint.

Decorative veneered   Plywood or blockboard panels overlaid in one or both faces with a decorative wood veneer such as afromosia, khaya, oak, sapele, or teak, ready for immediate installation and clear finishing.

Laminate-faced   Plywood panels surfaced with a range of coloured plastic laminates for many internal uses.

GRP-surfaced   Plywood panels overlaid with glass-fibre impregnated with polyester resins to give either smooth or matt surfaces. Provided in a range of colours, these panels provide decorative or hygienic surfaces which are very hardwearing. They have superior resistance to abrasion, chemicals and weathering and can be supplied taint-free for use with food stuffs.

Metal-faced   Plywood panels bonded to an aluminium sheet or patterned aluminium foil on one or both sides. They have good impact resist-

	Plywood	All birch	Birch faced (combi)	Conifer	Applied surfaces	Standard film faced	Heavy duty film faced	Decorative plastic film	Prepainted	Paper faced for painting	Decorative veneered	Laminate faced	Glass reinforced polyester	Glass reinforced phenol	Metal faced	Non slip surfaced	Rubber faced
Trucks and trailers																	
Floors	●	●												●		●	●
Sides	●	●				●	●		●	●			●	●	●		
Doors	●	●					●		●	●			●	●	●		
Taint-free surfaces									●				●				
Caravans																	
Floors	●	●	●			●	●						●				
Bodywork and fitments	●	●	●			●		●	●	●	●	●			●		
Buses and coaches																	
Floors	●	●					●						●			●	
Kick boards							●					●	●		●		●
Linings	●	●						●	●	●	●	●					
Luggage racks	●	●	●			●							●	●	●	●	●
Seats and back supports for upholstering	●	●	●														
Railway goods wagons																	
Sides	●	●					●								●	●	
Floors	●	●													●	●	
Railway passenger coaches																	
Interior linings and fitments	●	●	●			●	●	●	●	●	●	●			●		●
Freight containers																	
Floors	●												●			●	
Ordinary linings	●	●	●			●			●	●			●				
Doors	●	●											●		●		
Sides, roofs and ends for refrigerated containers	●	●							●				●				

Figure 147   *Guide to the use of plywood and surfaced-plywood panels*

ance together with the properties of the metal surface.

Rubber faced Plywood panels to which is bonded embossed rubber with good non-slip, sound-reducing, kick-proof and impact properties.

Non-slip surfaced Plywood panels surfaced with phenol resin or phenolic film and imprinted with a mesh pattern, patterned glass fibre or mineral aggregate bonded with a heavy resin content.

Machined and profiled Plywood and presurfaced plywood panels which are further processed in terms of shaping, cutting to size or drilling to customer's specific requirements. Standard or small panels of plywood can also be supplied tongued and grooved and also in built-up sections to provide profiled surfaces.

Guide to uses

The uses of plywood panels are tabulated in Figure 147.

14 Insulated/refrigerated bodywork

Vehicle noise

When commercial vehicles such as lorries and tractors or mobile construction equipment are to be treated for noise reduction, the first priority is to reduce the noise level as far as possible at source and isolate structure-borne vibrations using suitable flexible mountings (see Figure 148). Normally the power unit is mounted on such mountings but flexible mounting of the cab can also be beneficial. Residual noise can then be treated using appropriate acoustic materials.

For vehicles, the main problem is normally to reduce the noise level only in the cab or passenger compartment, though exterior noise may also be a problem.

Low-frequency engine noise (up to approximately 250 Hz) originates principally from the air intake and exhaust systems. These sytems should first be examined to check that there are no defects (corrosion, etc.) which are increasing the noise level. Consideration can also be given to re-locating the exhaust and intake openings as far from the cab as possible.

Further substantial reduction of low-frequency noise demands a redesign of the induction and exhaust systems which will normally be outside the scope of the user.

Higher frequency noise (about 1000 Hz upwards) emanates from the engine cylinder block and noise control by the user must consist of a combination of insulation, absorption and damping.

Insulation materials

Sound barrier material can be fitted to either or both sides of the panels between the noise sources and the cab, e.g. the bulkhead, bonnet cover or floor. The aim in all cases is to form a barrier which covers the whole area without gaps, to prevent noise entering the cab. It is important to avoid gaps in the barrier since a hole of only 0.1% of the area of a partition of 30 dB insulation can reduce the effectiveness by some 4 dB. If it is necessary for control cables, hoses, etc., to pass through the barrier mat, it is preferable to cut star-shaped slits rather than holes. The edges of the slits will then close up and reduce noise leakage. In addition, adequate sealing compound, gaiters or grommets should be used around the cable entry points.

At the frequencies normally encountered, a spaced-layer 'sandwich' type of barrier mat is

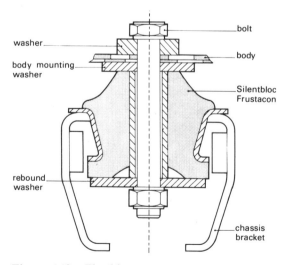

Figure 148 *Flexible mounting*

washer

body mounting washer

rebound washer

bolt

body

Silentbloc Frustacon

chassis bracket

more efficient than a single-layer type. It is desirable that the surface weight of the barrier mat should be at least equal to that of the surface to which it is applied, although this may not always be practical. As a general guide a material having a 5 kg/m^2 mass layer on a 12-mm self-extinguishing foam spacing layer is suitable for most applications in underbonnet and non-wear areas of the vehicle and is effective for frequencies over 350 Hz. The basic sound barrier materials, although tough, are not designed to withstand constant abrasion and wear. For exposed floor and toe board areas, an acoustic floormat is therefore recommended, incorporating a substantial ribbed-rubber layer to provide good wear resistance.

To minimize reverberation, the top, side and rear panels of the cab interior (see Figure 149) should be treated with an acoustic absorption material, such as acoustic foam of at least 25 mm thickness. In visible areas, trim foam having a suitable porous decorative facing can be used. Alternatively a perforated rigid panel backed by acoustic foam can be used. The load area should be treated in the same way. Undamped panels, especially large flat ones, will resonate in the audible frequency range. Suitable damping sheets must be stuck in place. On irregular surfaces, similar materials in paste form can be brushed or trowelled into place. As well as the noise reduction obtained, the apparent quality of the bodywork will be enhanced by the more 'solid' sound.

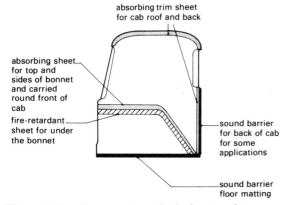

absorbing trim sheet for cab roof and back

absorbing sheet for top and sides of bonnet and carried round front of cab

fire-retardant sheet for under the bonnet

sound barrier for back of cab for some applications

sound barrier floor matting

Figure 149 *Cross-section of cab showing the areas that should be treated*

Fixing of acoustic materials

With the exception of vibration-damping material and mono-layer barrier mats, there is no need for the acoustic material to be in perfect contact with the surface to which it is applied. Fixing is therefore mainly a matter of providing location and can be by mechanical means (clips, etc.), by adhesives or, for horizontal surfaces, by laying the material in position.

Where mechanical fastenings are used, particularly with hanging curtains of sound barrier material, care should be taken that the material will not tear from its fastenings.

Conventional solvent-based adhesives may be attacked by the chemical plasticizers in the acoustic materials. This effect may take several months to become apparent and it is therefore advisable to use only the special adhesive approved as suitable for use.

Self-adhesive materials are not advised for use on curved or inverted surfaces when exposed to fluids, or at temperatures above 50°C.

With all adhesives, normal care needs to be exercised regarding ventilation, fire hazards, surface preparation, etc.

To summarize, there are four main ways of dealing with noise problems:

1 Reduce the noise level at source.
2 Apply noise-control measures.
3 Supply ear defenders.
4 Improve the acoustic environment.

To understand noise control methods, it is helpful to have some understanding of how noise is produced and transmitted. Noise is vibration of the air. The vibration can occur when there are pressure fluctuations ('pulses') in flowing air or when the surface of an object vibrates.

To explain how noise is transmitted, we can consider the analogy of a boat rocking on a pond. This will create waves which will travel out in all directions from the source of the disturbance. When the waves reach a sufficiently large solid obstruction, they are reflected back, so that we end up with a series of waves travelling to and fro. If the surface of the pond is crowded with reeds, it will be noticed that some of the energy of the waves is lost each time they force their way through the obstruction. Noise travelling through the air behaves in a similar way. When it strikes a dense object it will tend to be reflected and when it has to force its way through small pores in a material, it will lose some of its energy, i.e. it will be absorbed.

Properties of materials

The properties required in materials to deal with noise problems are:

1   *Damping*   Materials to reduce the vibration at source by reducing the amplitude of the resonant vibration.
2   *Insulation*   Material applied to partitions, enclosures, etc., to make them massive, helping them reflect the airborne sound waves instead of transmitting them through into the adjoining air space.
3   *Absorption*   Materials have tiny pores through which the air has difficulty in travelling and the vibration energy is dissipated as friction, thus reducing the intensity of the noise as it passes through the material. This property

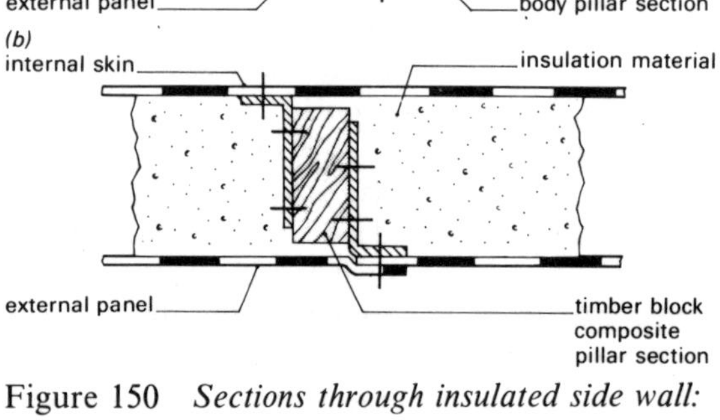

Figure 150   *Sections through insulated side wall: (a) with thermal bridge; (b) without thermal bridge*

is most usefully applied to prevent reverberation inside enclosures or reduce noise transmission inside ducts.

To a small extent, any material may exhibit these properties. However, specially designed acoustic materials have a much higher efficiency, can be chosen to deal with particular frequency ranges and are easy to apply.

Non-acoustic properties   In addition to their acoustic performance, materials may require other properties to meet particular application or service conditions, e.g. flammability resistance (various levels), wear and abrasion resistance, decorative coatings and surface coatings to prevent absorption of contaminants.

Refrigerated bodywork

Commercial vehicles built for refrigeration purposes may be classified as follows:

a   No thermal insulation.
b   With thermal insulation, the so-called 'half-isothermal' van.
c   With thermal insulation and specially designed bodywork to avoid 'thermal bridges'. These bodies are called 'isothermal' and have their own refrigeration unit which maintains a temperature below 0°C (see Figure 150).

The chief requirements of insulation materials used for refrigeration purposes are:

1   A low coefficient of thermal conductivity.
2   A high coefficient of vibration damping.

These properties are difficult to achieve simultaneously in any one material. Good thermal insulation properties can be obtained in materials which have included air bubbles but these make the materials non-elastic and elasticity is a necessary condition of vibration damping. In this situation, there are two possibilities:

a   The use of two materials, one of which has the appropriate damping qualities and the second of which gives thermal insulation and is placed on top of the first.

b The use of material with compromise properties, i.e. some of each.

The oldest material used for heat insulation, sheets of expanded cork with a relative density of 0.15, has been displaced by plastics which are lighter, cheaper and have better insulating properties. An example is expanded polystyrene with a relative density of 0.04. Others include:

Urea formaldehyde	0.03 – 0.04
Polyurethane	0.05 – 0.06
Neoprene	0.05 – 0.06

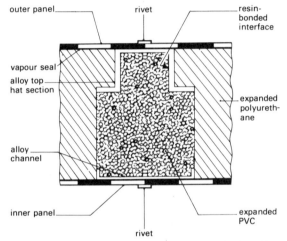

Figure 151 *Section through insulated body side wall*

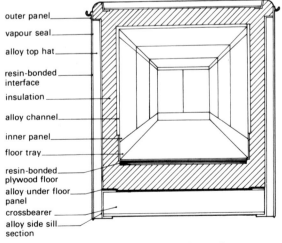

Figure 152 *Section through isothermal van*

The construction shown in Figures 151 and 152 results in complete isolation of the load compartment which is entirely surrounded by insulation. At no point is there a possibility of metal-to-metal contact which would impair its efficiency and the risk of moisture penetration, either from outside or inside during steam cleaning or washing out. As the PVC insulant is non-hygroscopic, it also provides a moisture barrier that water, entering, due to accidental damage, cannot pass, thus limiting the area affected and reducing the cost of repair.

Expanded polyurethane, because of its excellent insulation properties, is used as insulation between the frame pillars. Thickness of the insulation is varied according to the thermal requirement. Panels may be of aluminium alloy, or at some sacrifice in weight, of steel. The joints are sealed and close-pitch riveted and as additional insurance against the possibility of moisture penetration, a vapour seal is laid over the entire body surface before the outer panels are riveted to the frame. The rivets only penetrate into the non-hygroscopic insulation barrier and as an added precaution, these are of the completely waterproof sealed type.

In refrigeration-type bodywork, the two main causes of lost efficiency are vapour transmission and air leakage.

Experience has shown that a 12-tonne container body can accumulate as much as 1 tonne of water in sixteen months; this will more than double the heat transfer rate. This can be solved by using GRP construction of unbroken panel surfaces, both internal and external. Not only does this material resist water vapour transmission but it is an excellent insulant in its own right.

Many refrigerated van bodies are built around standard dry freight van shells. Depending upon the degree of insulation required, special depth low heat conductor spaces are fixed to the inside walls, roof and floor as stand offs to the interior structures at required insulation thickness. The most popular and by far the most efficient insulation medium is polyurethane foam which is sprayed in place filling all cavities to ensure maximum insulation efficiency.

The construction allows many options to be applied such as meat rails where special reinforcement is built into the roof structure to allow the whole cargo to be suspended from the roof. High-capacity mechanical refrigerator units or liquid-nitrogen refrigeration systems can be fitted. It is not enough to build a good low thermal conductivity body; the whole outer shell must be air-tight and water-tight to protect the insulation from the elements. All joints should be double compounded and bitumastically sealed. Door seals are extremely important in that they must be durable and provide an air-tight compression seal.

The flooring of the insulated vehicle is extremely critical in that it must support the cargo effectively and be a continuous waterproof membrane. Additionally, when carton loading with recirculating cooled-air refrigeration the floor structure must allow for airflow return. In the lower temperature zone body, a T-section continuous welded aluminium floor can be fitted with side wall flashings extended above the floor height to complete the watertight membrane.

Heat loss

The heat loss chart of Figure 153 shows the difference between three types of insulation graphically illustrated.

Comparison of insulation methods

The subject of actually insulating or foaming is a broad topic. Before any attempt is made by the bodybuilder to install foam, either by hand or by machine, the inner surfaces of the outer shell should be liberally coated with vapour-seal compound. This is a bituminous compound not unlike creosote in appearance, and is actually applied in a like manner. The idea of using this is three-fold:

1 It gives good adhesion for the foam.
2 It is ideally suited for filling small voids and hair-line gaps around sealant, rivet tails and extrusions.
3 It prevents ingress of any moisture into foam.

Following completion of foaming and after curing, all exposed surfaces of the foam should also be fully vapour-sealed. It is particularly important to do this immediately prior to installing the inner liner.

Much has been written and said on the credits and debits relating to *in situ* foaming as opposed to slab foaming by hand. As the expanding foam cools and solidifies against the inner face of the outer skin, a hard membrane is formed automatically on the outer surface of the foam. This is due to the temperature differentials of the dissimilar

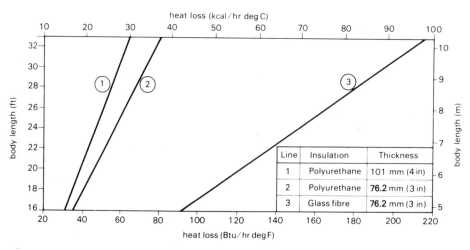

Figure 153   *Heat loss chart*

materials. At the same time, the foam secures a degree of adhesion to the inside of the outer skin, thereby increasing panel stiffness which, in turn, contributes to added impact resistance. This system also removes the often ignored task of applying vapour sealant before the outer skin is pop-riveted into position where the bodybuilder builds the inner framework first and then insulates, with the outer skin being applied last.

If carefully metered and executed, the *in situ* foaming technique ensures freedom from cavitation and results, overall, in an exceptionally strong insulated shell. The thermal efficiency of a unit so foamed will adequately ensure that it meets all existing requirements for the transport of perishables. There is a school of thought that casts suspicion and doubt on the efficiency of this foaming technique. In the early days, several companies attempting to utilize this technique, ran into the problem of cavitation which unfortunately does not become apparent until repairs are being made due to damage, or the cavity has taken on such an amount of water due to condensation that it literally bursts the inner lining during freezing.

The well established practice of slab foaming by hand can, if executed properly, prove to be quite acceptable. However, this depends on the use of high-quality, high-density foam and also on the vapour sealing used. Furthermore, one of the most serious problems encountered by operators is that of 'shake-down'. This is a popular term for the degradation that occurs when the unit is subjected to arduous operating conditions. This particularly applies to 12-m trailer units engaged in hauling hanging meat. The reason for this is that on undulating roads and/or poor road surfaces, the van shell can be subjected to extremes of twisting, thereby resulting in the slab stock cracking and breaking down. The net result of this over a prolonged period is cavitation with a resulting loss in thermal efficiency. To combat this, some quality-conscious bodybuilders employ a 'horizontal shelving' system. This is no more than a series of strips cut from heat break material and inserted at 300 to 450 mm intervals into the foam all the way down between the stiffeners.

Whilst not claiming to be an absolute guarantee that 'shake-down' will not occur, it does, nevertheless, drastically reduce the likelihood. This type of problem can be extremely prevelant on, say, a nominal quality unit built on a flexible trailer chassis at the same time operating on transcontinental routes or similar arduous journeys.

Another method that is gaining popularity is internal spray foaming. The bodybuilder constructs the outer shell and then proceeds to apply the foam with a spray gun. The main drawback is the toxic fumes given off and it is also very messy. After curing, the foam is trimmed back to the required thickness, usually with a hot knife (a large flat knife with a built-in heating element) to prevent the foam sticking. This process is time-consuming and afterwards may also require sanding in order to obtain a satisfactory smooth surface. When finished, the vapour sealing compound is liberally applied and then the inner lining attached.

Applications

It is essential that the bodybuilder determines exactly the nature of his customer's application. Some of the points which have to be considered are:

1 Temperature of load at time of entry into the closed van.
2 Total duration of journey, i.e. from leaving to returning to base.
3 Maximum number of likely door openings which will be experienced during the day (on full-width double rear doors this is obviously more vital than on, say, a single centre rear door).
4 Type of refrigeration unit to be employed.

Refrigeration methods

There are three popular methods of refrigerating commercial vehicle bodies: eutectic plates, mechanical units and liquid-nitrogen cooling.

Eutectic plates This is a well established system and is suitable where the total duration away from base is unlikely to exceed 12 hours per day. Obviously, after this a 'plug-in' facility is essential. It is not common practice to specify the plate system on multi-drop units in excess of 6 m in length.

The major drawback to plates is their weight. Four large-capacity plates on, say, a 4.2–4.8 m unit, could well weigh in at 700 kg. Very little progress has been made over the years with regard to the weight problem as the very nature of the eutectic solution means that heavy gauge steel is mandatory.

Plates are ordinarily installed on the side walls of units, but in order to prevent intrusion into the valuable load space, some operators insist that they are actually flush fitted into the insulation. The other alternative is to suspend them from the roof.

Mechanical units This is the most commonly understood method. The great advantage it has over all other systems is the degree of independence and mobility it gives the operator. Again, as a general statement, they are usually nose-mounted units (front wall). On a large reefer, the weight can add up quite easily to 0.75 tonne when installed. It is therefore essential that full precautions are taken during construction to adequately secure the reefer to the front wall and the front wall to the remainder of the van. This usually takes the form of extra bracings extended from the top of the front wall back approximately 2 to 3 m to the side walls and roof. The ones most commonly used are in the shape of thick (6 mm) plates cut diagonally and fitted prior to foaming.

Liquid-nitrogen cooling This is being more commonly employed, particularly in the fresh food sector. It consists very basically of a container (tank) to which are connected a series of small-bore copper pipes. These usually are installed at the upper extremities of the van running from front to rear. They have a series of jets at pre-determined centres along their full length through which the liquid nitrogen is sprayed during the 'pulling-down' process.

The freezing capability of this system is almost frightening. as the liquid 'boils-off' at –196°C, with the result that a fully loaded 12-m trailer unit can be 'pulled-down' in something approaching 3 minutes from ambient. Here again, if the unit is to be used on extra-long journeys, i.e. beyond a full day, provision must be made for topping up with coolent.

One of the most attractive features of this system is the very low weight involved in its installation. For instance, on a standard box body of, say, 4.8 m the saving over eutectic plate installation would be in the region of 50 kg. Not only does this give valuable added payload, but also greatly improved stability due to a reduced centre of gravity.

Several operators have found that the cost of a liquid nitrogen system can be rather expensive if not used correctly. This applies particularly where the unit is employed on multi-drop deliveries with a substantial amount of door openings. To combat this, several ideas have been formulated, one of which is the application of a heavy plastic blind installed in the doorway immediately behind the door itself. This prevents the in-rush of ambient air when the doors are opened, at the same time slowing down the rate at which the cold air leaves the vehicle. Overall, drivers do not like this due to the fact that they have to keep moving the heavy curtain to one side to gain access to the payload. Also, the automatic sensor has to be accurately set in order that the spray system does not cut in too frequently. On some installations, manual provision is made whereby the operator is able to give an extra 'squirt' in order to check any progressive rise in temperature during the day. Needless to say, this can prove very expensive if over-done. There is virtually no special reinforcement needed for the provision of a liquid-nitrogen system other than the odd steel bracket or stiffener necessary for the attachment of cylinders on the outside. One must always remember to wait two or three minutes after opening doors before entering.

This is to allow oxygen to enter the vehicle.

Air leakage

This is the common enemy of the refrigerated van. It is also, if not checked, akin to burning money. A surprising number of people seem totally unaware of the phenomenal leakage rates that can occur even in new and unused vans. For instance, it has been proven that on a new 12-m refrigerated trailer unit, having double rear doors (full width) and a single side door, when fitted with a nose-mounted reefer, it is possible to have a leakage rate of 9 m³ per hour.

Obviously, the prime areas of suspicion are the door seals. It is difficult to overestimate the very important and valuable job that this component has to do. Without adequate seals, all the quality foam, quality riveting, high-grade extrusions, premium sheet and skilled labour, etc., is wasted. Cryogenic gases substantially expand as they are exposed to atmosphere. Thus the interior of the van is slightly pressurized and slows down the leakage rate. It is therefore of paramount importance that only premium quality seals are used along with high tolerances in order that all the good work is not wasted.

Contraction and expansion

Generally speaking, all materials expand when warm and contract when cool. In refrigerated units, this is greatly emphasized, e.g. a 6-m unit experiencing a 60 degC temperature differential, i.e. ambient to interior, will be subjected to up to 6 mm of contraction. In effect, this means that some major components such as the floor, can actually measure 6 mm less than when installed. A 100 degC temperature differential can reportedly result in this being increased to 10 mm of difference in length between the outside and the inside. Tests have proven that a 12-m heavy-duty unit, operating in excess of a 100 degC temperature differential, can adjust its length by up to 16 mm depending on the type of construction and materials used.

Consider a reefer unit built in the bodyshop at say, 18°C operating in the Middle East with an ambient of 38°C and an inside temperature of –20°C. It does not leave much to the imagination as to what is happening to the structure and framework of that van. It is therefore essential in the interest of a long life, to use premium materials to offset the resulting cracks and fatigue that will inevitably occur.

15 Bus construction

General survey of bus body structures

The design of a bus body is based on the use of a light metal frame, braced by stressed metal panels. As with most other forms of transport, development has taken place from the early composite construction bodies, to the universally accepted all-metal structures of today.

The main framing of many bus bodies is constructed of light members of thin-gauge material formed according to the builder's design by folding, pressing, stretch forming, rolling or extrusion and connected by gussets generally riveted to the structure framework and, in most cases, applied on the inside face of the framing.

The exterior panelling is not considered as part of the structure, but merely serves to cover and protect the framework and to present a satisfactory exterior which, in the event of damage, can readily be replaced.

Whilst riveted structures are predominant at present, attention is being given to the increasing use of welding. This development needs very careful consideration in view of the more rigid nature of welded joints, since fatigue failures must be avoided.

Transverse stability is provided by the front and rear bulkheads and partitions and assisted in the case of double-decked vehicles by the upper deck floor or intermediate roof.

Many buses produced for export and many American vehicles have a body construction where the stress panels are applied on the exterior of the framework with neat lines of rivets in full view. With such a method of building for certain types of vehicles, it is possible to dispense with interior body side lining panels with a saving in

cost and weight. In considering the design of passenger service vehicles, whether single or double-deck, there are broadly three types of structure to be taken into account:

1 The orthodox type of body which is built as a complete separate unit, mounted on a chassis from which it is detachable (see Figure 154).

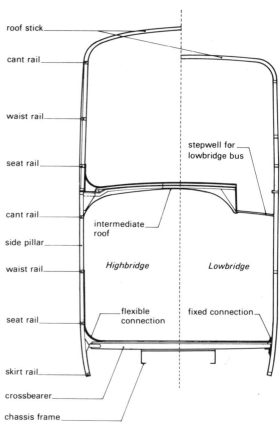

Figure 154 *Separate body and chassis construction*

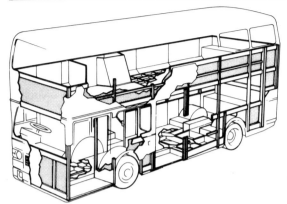

Figure 155   *All-metal integral construction of bus body*

2 The integral monocoque construction which incorporates an underframe into which are installed the power and running units (see Figure 155).

3 The semi-integral type of body, which although built as a unit, is permanently attached to a chassis frame, the two being designed to share, in complete unison, the loads imposed in service (see Figure 156).

In the separate body and chassis type of construction, the whole of the body and passenger load is transmitted to the springs by the chassis frame and it therefore becomes necessary to provide the body with transverse bearers of adequate strength to carry the load to the chassis, the crossbearers also being the foundation upon which the saloon floor is laid.

Many designs of floor bearer have been tried over the years with both rigid and flexible attachments to the body pillars and with both rigid and flexible mounting to the chassis. Experience has proved that in a double-decked orthodox type of vehicle the most important mounting points are those at the front and rear bulkheads. Between these points the sides of the body are designed to be sufficiently stiff to prevent undue deflections under load.

A bus body of this type is normally designed to require no support from the chassis beyond the rear spring-mounting points. The rear end of the body is cantilevered and chassis rear extensions are therefore not required. This type of bus body construction was superseded, first, by the low-line semi-integrals which posed new problems for body designers and now, after years of design, development and testing, the fully integral aluminium/steel-framed designs have emerged.

This type of vehicle, as its designation implies, has no separate chassis frame and therefore design considerations are very different from those of the chassis/body type. A substantial underframe is the first essential, since to this must be attached the power unit, transmission and running units. The underframe is not normally intended to convey the whole passenger load as does a chassis and therefore the bodysides and roof are designed as main load-carrying units. It follows that the sides and roof of a chassisless vehicle must be stronger and stiffer than those of the separate body and chassis type of vehicle.

Doorway openings must receive careful consideration and must be well reinforced longitudinally above the cant rail level, to compensate for the loss of side structure. On each side of the doorway stress bays it is advisable to ensure continuity of the side load-carrying beams.

The semi-integral type of structure has a complete chassis frame, which is built with outriggers to which the body sides are attached. It

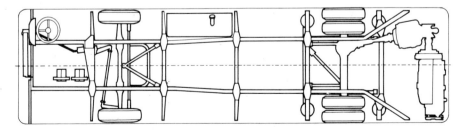

Figure 156   *Semi-integral chassis layout*

is not therefore necessary to include structural floorbearers in the body, a light framing being all that is required to carry the saloon floor.

The body is designed to share with the chassis the loads imposed in service and is usually attached permanently to the chassis outriggers, although in certain cases it can be made removable. Removal is obviously not so easy as with the separate body and chassis type vehicle.

Vehicles of the integral and semi-integral type achieve a lower overall height than the conventional chassis/body arrangement, the saloon floor being lower in height (with a consequent improvement from the passengers' point of view) and in step height from the road. The improved stability ensures a much greater factor of safety.

A double-deck bus arrangement is shown in Figure 157 and typical sections are shown in Figures 158–160.

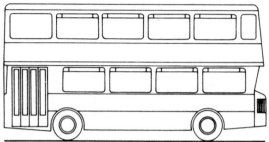

Figure 157 *Double-deck bus arrangement. For section details, see Figures 158–160*

Materials and equipment

Passenger vehicle design has responded to a demand for greater application of ergonomics, safety, noise control and improved maintainability. These factors have led to an increasingly wide range of materials and material processing techniques in the construction of bus bodies.

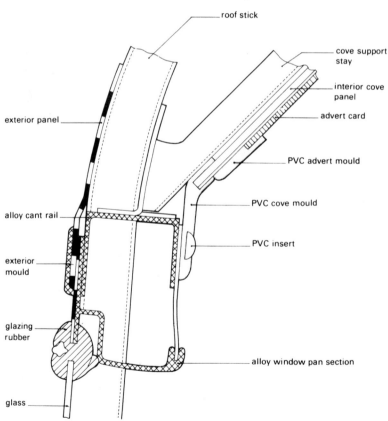

Figure 158 *Upper saloon cant rail*

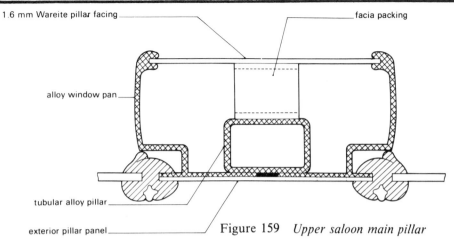

1.6 mm Wareite pillar facing

facia packing

alloy window pan

tubular alloy pillar

exterior pillar panel

Figure 159 *Upper saloon main pillar*

Integral understructure

The under section of an integral bus presents a challenge in the selection of materials and joining methods.

Metal gauges are thinner than those of the chassis side frames and it is as important to consider corrosion and fatigue resistance as it is to consider structural stiffness and strength factors. Galvanized steel, coated with zinc on each face, has been used successfully to provide corrosion

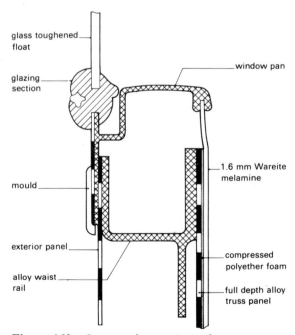

glass toughened float

glazing section

window pan

1.6 mm Wareite melamine

mould

exterior panel

compressed polyether foam

alloy waist rail

full depth alloy truss panel

Figure 160 *Lower saloon waist rail*

resistance. Resistance welding techniques for galvanized sheets require higher pressures and more frequent electrode dressings than are necessary for plain uncoated steel.

Aluminium sections have been used to fabricate bus structures for many years and the traditional alloys, HE15 and HE30 (BS 1474) are unlikely to be replaced by other developments in the foreseeable future. These alloys contain zinc, silicon and magnesium and have good corrosion resistance. **However, they should still be painted in underbody areas to prevent corrosion pitting, particularly in joint locations where a combination of fretting and the exclusion of oxygen under mud packs can lead to pitting which can, in turn, reduce fatigue life.**

Body materials (structural)

Glass-fibre-reinforced plastics, aluminium and low-carbon steel are the principle body structure and shell materials.

Corrosion protection

Corrosion problems in steel bus structures mainly consist of badly affected areas on valance panels and the lower parts of pillar sections. Hot-dip galvanized steel with additional painting is used to solve this problem. Recently, however, iron/zinc alloy coated steel has become available and has some potential advantages over the traditional galvanized product in that it is easier to weld and paint.

Zincro-metal, which is steel painted on-line with a proprietary zinc-rich coating, has been developed in the USA but has still to be evaluated in the UK. It could be a future competitor of galvanized and iron/zinc coated steels in the future.

Steel must be well painted in corrosion-susceptible areas whether or not it has a zinc coating.

Aluminium bodies are built mainly from HE30 alloy extrusions and N.S3 sheet (BS 1470). These alloys have good corrosion resistance, require less protective treatment than steel and in many parts of the bus, above the waist line, they can be left unpainted.

Panel bonding and sealing

Bus panelling is usually fastened by some form of riveting, often through an edge sealer strip. New techniques of weld bonding/rivet bonding offer advantages of higher joint strengths and fatigue life as well as better sealing against weathering.

Adhesives have become available which can attain high shear strength with a minimal amount of panel degreasing and preparation. A 10-mm wide strip of adhesive with a cured shear strength of 10 N/m^2 applied all round a panel creates a high strength joint. In practice, rivets or welds would also be used although in far fewer numbers than at present.

Loss of bond strength under conditions of high humidity or in corrosive environments is a potential problem necessitating extensive development work on surface treatments and adhesive modifications.

The potential *advantages* of bonding include:

1 Panel sealing accomplished.
2 Fretting and fatigue reduced.
3 High strength attained.
4 Reduced riveting.

There are some *disadvantages* in that:

1 Application techniques may be difficult to control.

2 The long-term effects of moisture on bond interface can be detrimental and must be subject to further research.
3 Panel removal difficulties must be resolved. Consideration has also to be given to the type of adhesives to be used. The designer will need to choose between high strength adhesives with little elasticity and lower strength ones with better elasticity.

Flooring

A bus floor is a structural section contributing to the overall vehicle body shell stiffness and carrying the passenger load. Tropical or European hard timber plywoods are generally selected and European woods are subsequently treated with an impregnation preservative to BS 4072. Recently European hard timber plywoods with a preservative applied at the glue line during manufacture have become available. These offer possibilities of improved distribution of the preservative salts.

Fire-retardant properties are desirable in bus floors and many are treated to the requirements of BS 476, Class 1, in single deckers and in the lower saloon of double deckers. Treatment can either be with an impregnation process or with an intumescent coating applied to the underside of the floor.

Composite floors with lightweight cores have been investigated to achieve weight savings and improved thermal insulation. High manufacturing costs and a tendency for de-lamination to occur in service must be overcome before such floors can be accepted for general use.

Fatigue properties of structure

The fatigue life of bolted, riveted and welded joints varies according to a number of parameters, including the following:

1 Parent metal combination.
2 Material surface finish.
3 Bolt/rivet or weld type.
4 Hole clearance.
5 Method of hole forming.
6 Clamping force.

For example, drilled and riveted joints in aluminium generally fail under the rivet head due to fretting. In the case of aluminium with punched holes, the failure occurs between the plates or under the rivet and the fatigue endurance limit is lower than that for drilled holes. This seems to be due to the formation of a deformed area around the periphery of the punched hole. This creates a raised and irregular contact area under the bolt head or against the opposing aluminium plate, depending on which way round the sections are bolted together. Accelerated failure is then initiated by fretting as before.

Galvanized steel plates riveted together exhibit better fatigue life than painted mild steel due to the galvanized coating smearing under fretting action and resisting penetration of the wear damage into the underlying steel.

Body material (non-structural)

The interior design and styling of modern passenger service vehicles is influenced not only by comfort considerations, but also by factors such as safety, ease of cleaning and maintenance, vandal resistance and aesthetics. A wide variety of metals and plastics are used to achieve the performance demands.

Floor tread materials

A further important part of the total floor is the tread surface or floor facing material. This is a critical item in terms of wear resistance and passenger safety. Floor facing materials are tested for the following characteristics:

a   Wear resistance.
b   Elongation and tensile strength.
c   Compression set.
d   Coefficient of friction (wet and dry) on various shoe materials.
e   Dimensional stability.
f   Water absorption.
g   Fire retardance.

Seating

The driver's and passenger's seats are built to different design requirements to account for their different functions but are both upholstered and trim-finished to a high standard.

Foam cushioning for drivers' seats has generally been of natural rubber latex which has good compression set resistance. Synthetic cold-cure polyether/urethane is now competitive with latex and can also be formulated to give good fatigue properties and high hysteresis values.

Seat foams for passengers are usually cold-cured materials but they sometimes have sections or inserts of hot-cure foams or chip foams.

Seat covering materials are selected from a choice of hide, PVC-coated fabric, 100% synthetic fibre yarn or moquette. Typical material weights (PVC *plus* fabric) are 0.34 kg/m² for a low-duty application to 0.90 kg/m² for high-duty expanded air permeable coverings. These types of covering are widely used on drivers' and passengers' seats. They can be colour-printed and dielectrically welded. PVC also has good wear resistance and is easily cleaned. One of the newer developments being evaluated is PVC on a wool/synthetic felt.

Nylon, polyester and acrylic raised and cropped warp-knitted synthetic fibre yarns are applicable to driver and passenger seats.

Woven moquettes in the form of wool, cotton and nylon blends are very popular for PSV passenger seating. They are produced in attractive patterns, have good aesthetic value and are well proven for durability. Weight for weight, wear resistance is not as good as that of 100% knitted nylon, but this is compensated for by the extra weight of material used to construct a moquette.

There is always controversy over which material to select for cleanability and vandal resistance. PVC is the easiest to clean *in situ* but moquette covers can often be removed completely and washed at intervals. All of the materials are prone to vandalism, but the textile materials are possibly less frequent targets.

Passenger seat construction in a bus is generally steel tubular frame with plywood base and back and a melamine-faced phenolic laminate on the back for styling and for resistance to vandalism. Some seats are now constructed entirely from melamine-faced laminates on wood; others from GRP shells. Experimentation in seat design and materials for passenger and driver is being undertaken at present in various sectors of the industry.

Trim panels

The large flat or single-curvature wall and ceiling areas of a PSV are frequently covered with melamine-faced plastic laminates. They are specified to incorporate a number of important features such as decorative finishes, a variety of gloss conditions, cleanability, impact resistance and fire resistance. These properties are governed by a number of international and British Standards.

Decorative laminated sheet can be bonded to aluminium or stainless steel. Bonded to aluminium, the composite has low weight, stability under various climatic conditions and better safety performance in impact than the laminated plastic sheet alone.

Plastic phenolic laminates are unsuitable in areas where there is curvature in more than one plane. In such cases, glass-fibre-reinforced polyester mouldings are generally used. They have the required surface finish and, if properly designed, will have the required mechanical characteristics. They can be manufactured by a variety of techniques ranging from the labour-intensive, low tooling cost, hand lay-up methods, to the low labour content, higher tooling cost, hot compression moulding methods using prepared glass/resin mixtures such as dough moulding compounds (DMC) and sheet moulding compounds (SMC). The choice of technique depends upon whether the item is only 'one off' per vehicle such as a front upper saloon trim panel or the heater pod on a roof where a hand lay-up method is the most cost-effective. For items such as a complete window shroud with perhaps 10 in a single deck vehicle and 20 in a double decker, then compression moulding is the answer.

Insulation

Thermal insulation of the vehicle interior is a major consideration. The floor, side panels and the roof all constitute potential routes for major heat losses from inside. These losses can be minimized by careful choice of flooring materials and incorporating still-air gaps and foam materials into the side and roof structures. Some buses have a sprayed foam in the roof structure which, apart from excellent thermal and sound insulation properties, also meets Class 1 of BS 476, Part 7: 'Surface spread of flame of building materials'.

Windows

The Motor Vehicles (Construction and Use) Regulations, 1978, No. 1017, specifies that all windows fitted in motor vehicles shall be safety glass, and the Public Service Vehicles (Conditions of Fitness, Equipment and Use) Regulations, 1972, No. 751, states that where a vehicle is fitted with a front windscreen for the driver, the windscreen shall, except where an adequate demisting and defrosting device is fitted, be capable of being opened so as to give the driver a clear view of the road ahead.

The main requirements of a vehicle windscreen to meet reliability and safety requirements are:

1   High transparency and freedom from visual distortion.
2   External durability to reduce surface degradation and scoring from wipers, ice scrapers, gritty road spray, etc.
3   Vision not materially affected by normal road stone impact.
4   Retention of impacting occupant with low deceleration to avoid brain damage.
5   Fragment formation should not expose the face and head to risk of severe laceration.
6   Freedom from faults which will interfere with vision.
7   Be capable of withstanding normal treatment in the service for which it is supplied.

The general definition of safety glass in accordance with BS 857:1967 'Specification for safety glass for land transport is 'a glass which if fractured is less likely to cause severe cuts or serious injury than ordinary glass'. Ordinary annealed glass is toughened and made into safety glass by a process of pre-stressing which consists of heating the pre-cut glass in a furnace to nearly its softening point. The glass is then chilled suddenly by compressed air delivered from a large number of jets. This hardens the outer surfaces which are pulled inwards and put into compression by the hot inner core as it cools and contracts. When completely cool, it is encompassed by a uniform envelope of compression with a balancing tension in the centre. If fractured, it disintegrates into small, blunt, harmless pieces. In general, its liability to fracture under the action of external forces or changes of temperature is greatly reduced by the toughening process.

Toughened windscreen glass has a zone of modified heat treatment in which the fragmentation, if the glass is fractured, comprises sufficient pieces of larger size than elsewhere to afford better vision through the zone than through the remainder of the glass. Laminated safety glass is popular for windscreens because it does not disintegrate on fracture and vision is retained. It consists of two or more pieces of annealed glass firmly united to and alternating with one or more pieces of reinforcing material known as 'interlayer' (clear plastic). Fracture does not cause the glass to separate from the interlayer to any substantial extent and in general the laminate does not break into large fragments.

The latest type of safety windscreen retains the best features of existing toughened and laminated glass. It consists of a high-stressed inner glass ply bonded to a low-stressed outer glass ply by a high-penetration-resistant plastic interlayer. If, in an accident, a person's head should hit and break the windscreen, then the contact area will fragment into fine relatively blunt particles, nearly all of which will remain bonded to the interlayer. The plastic interlayer serves to cushion the impact and to retain the occupant within the vehicle, giving protection against injury from external objects.

As with a conventional laminated windscreen, a sharp flying roadstone can produce a small star or cone break in the outer glass, but the windscreen cannot disintegrate as happens with a toughened windscreen; visibility is therefore retained and the vehicle can continue in use.

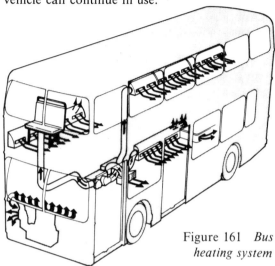

Figure 161 *Bus heating system*

Heating

A typical heating system for a double-deck bus (see Figure 161) may employ two radiators with twin blowers, both units housed below the staircase on top of the off-side front wheelbox.

Fresh air from an intake in the exterior panelling below the waist is ducted down between the skins to the blowers and hot air to the lower saloon is ducted through the rear staircase panel to an aluminium alloy duct, along the off-side floor cove, with outlets below each two passenger seats and ducted below the rear raised floor to the outlet in the gangway riser panel. Hot air to the upper saloon is ducted up the rearward corner of the stairwell to the full-length aluminium alloy duct along the off-side floor cove, with outlets below each two passenger seats. The duct in the stairwell is usually covered with a moulded GRP finisher. The air intakes are baffled against ingress of water and are fitted with glass-fibre filter units. The heater units are controlled by two switches on the saloon lighting board wired through a suitable relay. A minimum number of piping connections are made with compression joints where possible and flexible connections made where necessary. The hot water supply to all the heater units is separate from the engine cooling system.

Saloon lighting

A large double-deck bus usually requires eleven 900-mm, 30-W daylight fluorescent tubes (six in the upper saloon, five in the lower). The tubes are in surface-mounted enclosed fittings in the cornice panels of both saloons.

Entrance step lighting normally consists of an enclosed light fitting with bulb mounted to the centre of the step well risers and operated by a micro-switch in the door gear system, mastered by the side and tail lamp switch.

The route indicator box lighting is usually two 600-mm, 20-W daylight white fluorescent tubes in batten-type holders controlled by an adjacent transistor ballast on a separate switch on the saloon switchboard.

Styling considerations

The stylist of passenger service vehicles works under quite severe engineering restraints. Also the product volume of PSVs may only be one or two per cent of the volume from a car manufacturer, perhaps less than 50 units per week. Consequently, the production methods for PSV trim parts must not usually involve high tooling costs.

Colour schemes, curvature of trim panels and hidden fixings are areas where an individual stylist can exert his influence on the bus interior.

Ergonomists, human-factor engineers, also take a hand in the style and layout of modern vehicles. Their contribution is invaluable in adequately assessing in scientific terms the needs of passengers and crew members. If their job is well done, then their influence is reflected in the comfort, safety and convenience of the passengers and the undistracted concentration of the driver.

The changes occurring in PSV material specifications are not radical but are occurring in a continuous progression. Developments in corrosion-resistant coatings have been utilized

and new materials show promise for the future. Radical material and process changes to such systems as composite floors and the use of adhesive bonding techniques are still future possibilities. Traditional body structure panel materials are unlikely to change in the foreseeable future.

The increasing cost of materials and energy creates a necessity for improvements in material utilization, longer-life corrosion resistance and the use of spray-on thermal insulation being just two examples.

Bus construction in knock-down kit form

The advantages of building bodies using fabricated kits and components can be outlined as follows:

1 The supply of components in completely knocked-down condition gives great savings in freight charges.
2 Kit assembly is simple and requires only semi-skilled operatives.
3 All design and drawing office work is undertaken for the customer, to his requirements.
4 Savings in cost are made because the components are fabricated with specialized equipment.
5 The alternative methods of supply enable individual companies to purchase in the way that makes best use of their own resources.

Framing

Materials used in the construction are cold-rolled steel sections, high-tensile steel tubing and high-tensile light alloy extrusions.

Kit contents

1 An arrangement drawing showing the item number and location of each item.
2 A schedule of parts which details the item no., drawing no. and quantity of each part.
3 A bolt list showing type, size, length, location and quantity of each nut and bolt.

Complete structures are assembled with high-tensile bolts and wedglock nuts which make secure body joints that will not loosen in service.

Protection

All components are fully protected; they are degreased, phosphated, dipped in a specially formulated red oxide chromate primer and stoved at 220°C for 15 minutes. This process gives a tough durable finish of exceptionally high quality.

Methods of supply

Fully fabricated kit This is a kit consisting of a complete body framing ready to bolt together. It is recommended for quantity production and will give the maximum output from existing floor space and labour force. It is ideally suited to the smaller company which receives orders in excess of production capacity.

Partly fabricated kit with straight material Pillars, crossbars and roofsticks are supplied fully fabricated for erection, together with sufficient straight lengths of section to enable the customer to manufacture the remaining portion of the structure. This kit is suitable for smaller quantity production or production of a varied nature.

Bends and straight material Swept and bent parts are supplied with standard brackets and gussets for the customer to complete the fabrication as required. Straight lengths of section are also supplied to make up the remainder of the structure.

Miscellaneous structural items Individual items such as roofsticks, cross-bearers, pillars, wheel-arches, doors, etc., are supplied from stock. Pillars and cross-bearers can be supplied assembled or as loose items for the customer to assemble to his own requirements.

Finishing items Panels, both flat and shaped, windows, seats and other components can be supplied in addition to the framework.

Sequence of operations

The sequence for building is as follows:

1 Chassis preparation (Figure 162). The floor frame is placed in position, holding-down bolts fixed and all parts of the chassis painted.
2 The body side framing and front end is assembled (see Figure 163), truss panels bolted into position, the body lined up with the waist rail and the lower bolts tightened.
3 The body ends and roof framing are positioned and fixed, the wheelboxes and entrance steps installed (see Figure 164).
4 Truss panels between the waist rail and seat rail over the wheel-arches are riveted into position (see Figure 165).
5 General inspection of finished framing to ensure all structural bolts are tight and truss panels securely riveted (Figure 166).
6 Flooring and interior lining panels fixed and riveted into position.

Figure 162 *Chassis preparation*

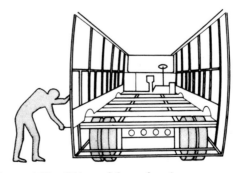

Figure 163 *Side and front framing*

7   Roof panels are fixed and riveted (Figure 167).

8   Side windows are riveted, windscreens fixed, inside ceiling panels, mouldings, pillar cappings and electric light fittings fixed (Figure 168).

9   Tubular seat frames are positioned and bolted through the floor and seat rail. Extra floor covering and treads fixed; stanchions and grab handles are fitted.

10 Final finishing and inspection (Figure 169).

Figure 164   *Roof framing and rear end*

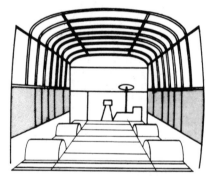

Figure 165   *Truss panels rivited*

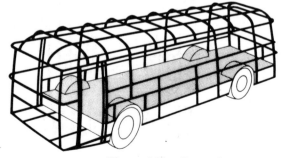

Figure 166   *General inspection*

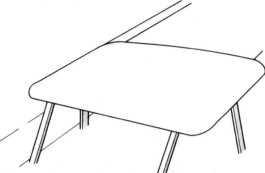

Figure 167   *Roof panels*

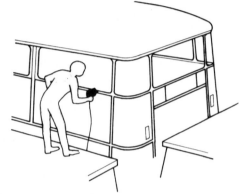

Figure 168   *Panelling and moulding*

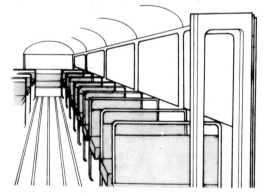

Figure 169   *Final finishing*

PSV door systems

A wide range of door systems is produced by specialist manufacturers who offer bodybuilders a choice of various door types and operating systems to suit almost any requirement. Doors are powered by pneumatic or electric actuators mounted overhead.

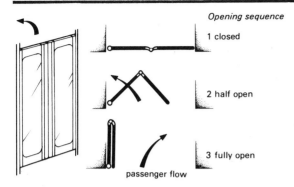

Figure 170 *Single folding door: the free edge of the door is guided by a roller running in an overhead track*

Single folding door (Figure 170)

Advantages:
Particularly suitable for entrance doors.
Wide unobstructing opening.
Maximum visibility for driver.
Opened door does not impede passenger flow.

Disadvantage:
Unsuitable where floor is stepped near doorway.

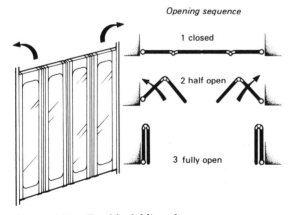

Figure 171 *Double folding doors*

Double folding doors (Figure 171)

Advantages:
Wide opening suitable for entrance or exit doors.
Small inwards swing allows floor to be stepped over chassis.

Disadvantages:
Reduced visibility compared with two-leaf doors.
Reduced clear doorway width, i.e. reduced by four times the leaf thickness.

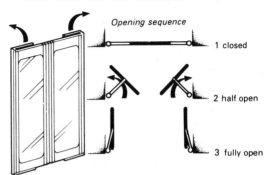

Figure 172 *Inward gliding doors*

Inward gliding doors (Figure 172)

Advantages:
Particularly suitable for mid-vehicle exit doors.
Can be near-flush with outside of vehicle.
Large glass area.
Large clear width of opening (reduced by only twice the leaf thickness).

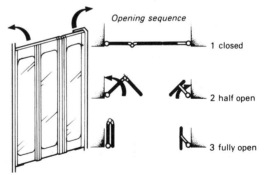

Figure 173 *Two-plus-one folding/gliding combination doors*

Two-plus-one folding/gliding combination doors (Figure 173)

For applications where a step in the floor precludes the use of single folding or twin-gliding doors. This arrangement still provides a good clear glass area and a wide door opening.

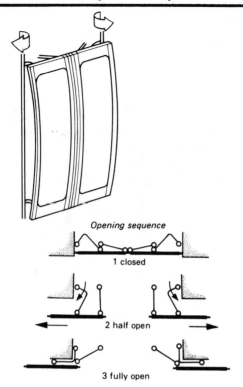

Opening sequence

1 closed

2 half open

3 fully open

Figure 174   *Outward gliding doors*

Outward gliding doors (Figure 174)

Advantages:
Unobstructed doorway.
Flush fitting doors.
Suitable for curved doors.

Disadvantages:
Cannot be opened when vehicles are closely parked.
Some applications in UK limited by PSV regulations.
Hinge arms project into vehicle.

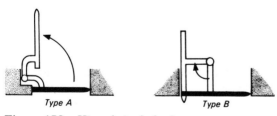

Type A   Type B

Figure 175   *Hinged single leaf*

Hinged single-leaf door (Figure 175)

Type A is suitable for single-leaf doors up to 600 mm wide and Type B is more suitable for curved doors, e.g. on luxury coach bodies, but requires a step to cover the lower hinge.

Following glider door

This is mainly used for curved doors. The primary leaf opens normally like a folding door and the secondary leaf pivots on an arm like a gliding door. Thus, in the 'open condition' the two leaves are 'nested' together to give a maximum clear opening. This avoids excessively projected hinges as would be required if the curved leaves were folded normally.

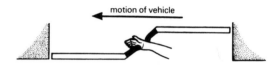

motion of vehicle

Figure 176   *Offset doors*

Offset doors (Figure 176)

Offset door leaves are a special safety feature whereby the rubber nosings are arranged to be set at an angle of 40° to the door surface. This allows a trapped limb to be readily released as a result of the forward movement of the vehicle, with no conscious effort on the part of the passenger.

Shelf-plate mechanism

The layout of the pneumatic shelf-plate mechanism is shown in Figure 177.

Basic door-control system

Control may be either all-pneumatic or electro-pneumatic. In general, all-pneumatic systems are more reliable and cheaper. If electrical inputs are required to the control system (from motion-sensing devices on the vehicle's transmission, or from door-obstruction detecting devices, for example), then it is necessary to introduce

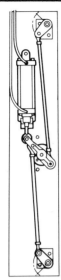

Figure 177 *Layout of pneumatic shelf-plate mechanism*

solenoid valves into the control system, i.e. to use an electropneumatic system.

Control methods

There are several ways of operating each type of system:

All-pneumatic:
1 Direct air – operated directly by driver's hand-control valve.
2 All-pneumatic air-bleed spool valve – operation by pneumatic push-buttons.

Electropneumatic:
1 Electropneumatic control by driver – direct air emergency controls.
2 Electropneumatic control by driver – air bleed push-buttons for emergency control.
3 Electropneumatic control by driver – electrical push-buttons for emergency control.

There are also many variants (*each* applicable to some, but not all, of the above systems), e.g.

a Single door or twin door (entrance and exit) vehicles.
b Control of doors by a sixth position on the driver's gear selector.
c Foot controlled by driver.
d Push-button or rocker-switch driver's control.
e Obstacle detection.
f Transmission speed-sensing interlocks.
g Door-closed detection (operating warning devices or interlocks).
h Isolation of one leaf of a twin-leaf door (in light traffic or cold conditions).

Safety features

Safety is of paramount importance and after continuous development and testing programmes over many years, many safety features are now built into power-operated door systems for passenger vehicles. These safety features include:

1 Offset door leaves designed to allow for a trapped limb to be automatically released as a result of the forward movement of the vehicle – these do not rely on electropneumatic or electromechanical devices so no maintenance is required.
2 Photo-electric beam. Door closes automatically at pre-determined time after the last alighting passenger passes through.
3 Gear shift lock, preventing selection of gear whilst exit doors are still open.
4 Electrical-sensitive edge on exit door causes automatic opening if obstruction is encountered.
5 Pneumatic-sensitive edges giving audible and visual warning to the driver of door obstruction.
6 Transmission interlock preventing opening of doors whilst vehicle is in motion.
7 Tread mats with provision to either reverse the door movement or provide audible visible warning to the driver.

16 Luxury coach bodywork

General design considerations

Within the manufacturing tradition of the separate chassis and body construction, British coach styles have mostly retained their own distinctive appearance, despite the influence of integrally constructed coaches from the European continent. Brightwork and metal trim continue to be used in large amounts despite the fashion of paint-against-paint liveries without the addition of so many trims and mouldings.

Continental coachbuilders are increasingly adopting designs to suit British chassis as trade barriers tumble and currencies begin to level with one another. The terms of trade still have a long way to go before competition becomes intense, but a number of imported body styles are already available.

The trend towards low profile tyres has not yet got into its stride with coaches but because of the continuing reduction in aspect ratios of car tyres, for stability and handling reasons that apply also to coaches, this present lull might not endure for very long. Tyre manufacturers are well aware of the advantages of lower profiles and can be expected to welcome any moves in this direction by the chassis manufacturers.

Aerodynamically, a single-decker coach has two advantages over most other types of vehicle; not only is its aspect ratio (in both side elevation and plan view) quite high, but also it is less sensitive than a truck, for instance, to the side-effects of such elementary aerodynamic aids as putting a decent radius on the corners, avoiding encroachment on seating room. It has been suggested that aerodynamic drag coefficients as low as 0.35 are practicable for buses and coaches. Increased rake of the windscreen and curvature of the front are beneficial, although both could impose limitations on the front single entrance door design. A projecting frontal dome for a destination board militates against aerodynamic efficiency as do unfaired mirrors and some roof-mounted ventilators which create interference drag.

There is much less scope for a frontal air dam on a coach than on the average truck cab, since the nose panelling is extended nearer to the ground in any case. A properly designed air dam could however result in a significant reduction in drag but it would require a wind tunnel programme to evaluate this and other aerodynamic aspects of the coach.

One aspect of the overall aerodynamics is directly chassis-orientated. It is the relationship between the centre of pressure and the centre of gravity, a relationship that has a major influence on high-speed stability. Drivers have commented that at speed, rear-engined coaches tend to weave unpleasantly in gusty conditions. This directional instability must be due to the centre of gravity being further to the rear than when the engine is 'amid-ships' or at the front; owing to the basic constraints the shape cannot be altered sufficiently to bring the centre of pressure far enough aft to compensate. One can conclude that the rear-engined layout is really best avoided for high-speed coaches unless aerodynamic correction can be built into the body shape.

Modern luxury coaches are designed and developed to meet the increased demand for safety and comfort that will be required by legislation.

Passenger comfort and safety are being combined with smart exteriors and attractive interiors.

Many pre-production models successfully complete thousands of miles on the severe pave circuit at the Motor Industry Research Association testing grounds whilst others are proven in actual operating services on some of the toughest and longest coach routes across Europe.

The design, development and testing of new British luxury coaches has to ensure that they meet European regulations such as roof loadings, passenger seat strength, driver's rear vision, front and rear lighting (including dual level). The overall style and design is arranged so that future European demands can be readily incorporated in later production without the need for major redesign.

The Department of Transport says that the PSV (Conditions of Fitness, Equipment and Use) Regulations, 1972, are still and will remain fully in effect. EEC Regulation 36 describing uniform provisions concerning the construction of public service vehicles is not effective in Britain and countries who ratify EEC Regulation 36 will be able to 'E' mark coaches which comply with this regulation either for use in their own country or for export. However, EEC Regulation 36 does not cover the full requirement for the UK and therefore a number of Conditions of Fitness Regulations will still need to be complied with before an operating licence can be issued. For the immediate future, the vehicle builders in this country will therefore have to meet the Conditions of Fitness Regulations, 1972, or meet EEC Regulation 36 plus various Conditions of Fitness requirements. EEC Regulation 36 includes additional regulations covering loading conditions, number of passengers carried, strength and a multi-function emergency switch. It also requires a minimum of five exits, including emergency exit windows, on coaches with more than thirty-five seats plus one escape hatch in the roof.

Passengers suffer badly from heat in hot weather so extra roof lights should be fitted, say four between the existing five in a 12-m body, one of which would be an escape hatch to comply with EEC Regulation 36. With eight roof lights open at the front end, enough air should be scooped in when moving to keep the interior cool; the rearmost rooflight opens at the back to act as an air exit. Fine wire mesh in front of the rooflights keeps insects out and these extra rooflights would help prevent the interior of the coach heating up like an oven when parked in hot sunshine.

Interior noise reduction can be achieved by raising the body by the amount by which the wheel-arches intrude and filling the space with sound deadening material (acoustic cladding) over the major noise-producing machinery such as engine, fans, transmission including rear axle, exhaust and air intakes. Acoustic cladding can be placed on the side panels so that engine noise reflected off the road surface would not be transmitted to the inside of the coach. The present space above the engine could be retained for cooling air. When both engine and wind noise are reduced, tyre noise becomes the main component of over-all noise and this can be reduced by a layer of acoustic cladding inside the wheel-arches. Exhaust noise could be reduced by increasing the size of the silencer and leading the exhaust pipe to the back of the coach instead of finishing it at the rear wheels. Exterior features of coach bodies include stainless steel front grilles and imposing side mouldings in the same highly polished material, large functional rear lamps and their surrounds and deep curved passenger windows.

Encompassing the body at maximum width the new rubber hollow section bumpers absorb the minor bumps and scrapes. The large over-riders at the front and rear extreme points add their protection and serve as footsteps to enable windscreen cleaning to be carried out.

Passenger safety

This aspect is of paramount importance in coach design. Starting with ample driver vision, driving lights, large front and rear obligatory lamps and dual-level direction indicators, the size of the illuminated areas making their message unmistakable and matching the large vehicle to which they are fitted.

The tail-lamp has especially been increased in area and twin bulbs give more illumination and added protection in the event of one bulb failing. The twin passenger seats are tested to retain the passengers seated behind them, in line with the proposed 'seat strength requirement'.

Comfort, safety and the ease with which the trim can be changed are some of the main requirements of coach seating. New coach seats have been developed that make use of steel tubular frames and substantial cast aluminium brackets, cushioning of latex foam and a sprung mattress to give support to the back.

Dynamic tests with dummies have shown that these new seats can withstand the Department of Transport recommendation in crash testing of 8g with a 100% safety factor, while static tests have shown that under a load of 570 kg, the individual backrests are deformed by only 125 mm whereas the permitted deformation is 200 mm at 450 kg. Foam-filled crash pads and dough-moulded GRP finisher panels also give controlled deformation under crash conditions. To eliminate the need for re-upholstering, the seats have detachable backrest panels and the tailored seat covers can be removed and replaced in a matter of minutes.

The recliner type of seat, with armrests, weighs 36 kg, each assembly consisting of two seats. The fixed type seat weighs 29 kg trimmed, the frame weighing only 14 kg.

Parcel racks

The new type parcel racks of suspended design incorporate ducts supplying fresh air from the roof intake scoop to the overhead passenger outlets in twin vent and light units. The vents are opened and closed by twisting, the reading lights are individually switched and the whole unit fitted above the surface of the welded pattern foam trim panels to give increased protection and reduced hostility in the event of accidents. The ducts also provide demisting to the passenger windows through individually controlled roll-over vents. The hanging brackets and all-metal framing is heavily nylon coated to give complete protection

Figure 178   *Luxury coach*

to passengers' clothing, etc., and both edges of the rack are finished with Formica reliefs.

Entrance

The entrance door can be manual or power-operated leading to a well designed step well which has non-slip nosing and special-purpose handrails fitted with 'Netlon' grip sleeving (see Figures 178 and 179).

Driver's position

The whole of the interior front has a Formica cabinet and gives improved accessibility to the vital components mounted on a large instrument binnacle (made of ABS). The switch panel is illuminated and has ISO symbol identification. Illuminated rotary controls are positioned for the demisters/heaters using high volume piping to the moulded dual outlets at the base of the windscreen.

The driver's seat features a deeply contoured, high-support backrest and large bucketed cushion with latex foam filling for maximum comfort. To the off-side of the driver there is a locker for the driver's personal use and in addition

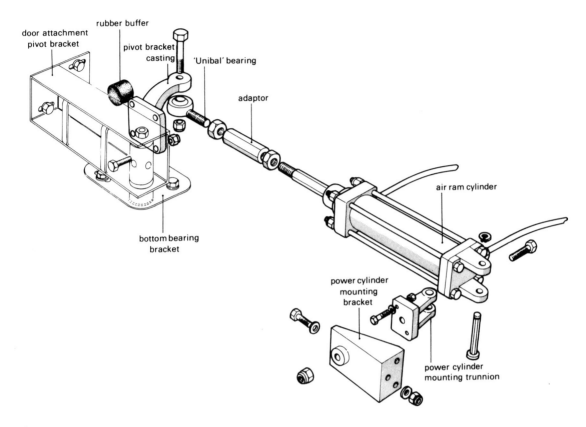

Figure 179   *Arrangement of power-operated door mechanism*

to the footlevel heater/ventilator outlet, the binnacle has twin fresh-air face-level outlets, the off-side being capable of demisting the signalling window when required.

The driver's environment is completed by a moulded headboard fitted with a recessed battery clock and concealed sun visor.

Through the twin front screens, the driver has a wide range of vision, a very large area being swept by the blades of two-speed pantograph wipers.

Construction and panelling (Figures 180 and 181)

The body incorporates rectangular section steel body bearers in GR50C material with heavy section 'U' channels welded to the ends for attachment to the 'U' section steel side pillars using high-tensile bolts.

The pillars have hardwood filling to take the side panel fixings and terminate at the top of the windows where they are welded to the rolled box-section cant rail. The cant rails at each side locate into a rolled section that forms the outer members of the all-steel box-section welded roof, the whole framework making a structure of great strength to meet the proposed roof loadings and anticipated roll-over requirements. The framework for the front and rear assemblies are also of steel welded construction, supporting the moulded glass-reinforced plastics back and front panelling (see Figures 182 and 183).

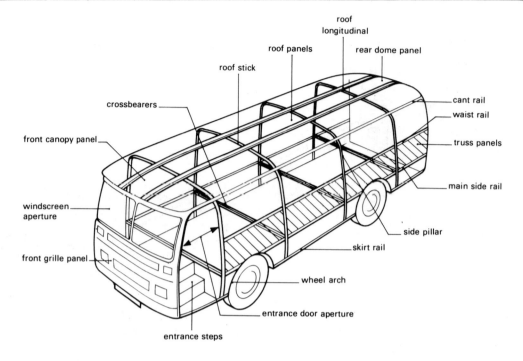

Figure 180 *Part names and locations*

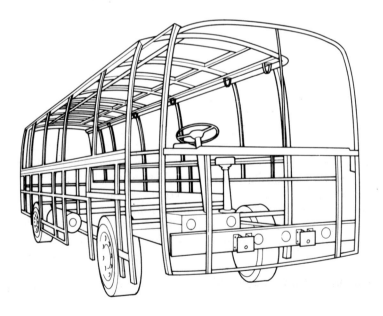

Figure 181 *Typical coach structure*

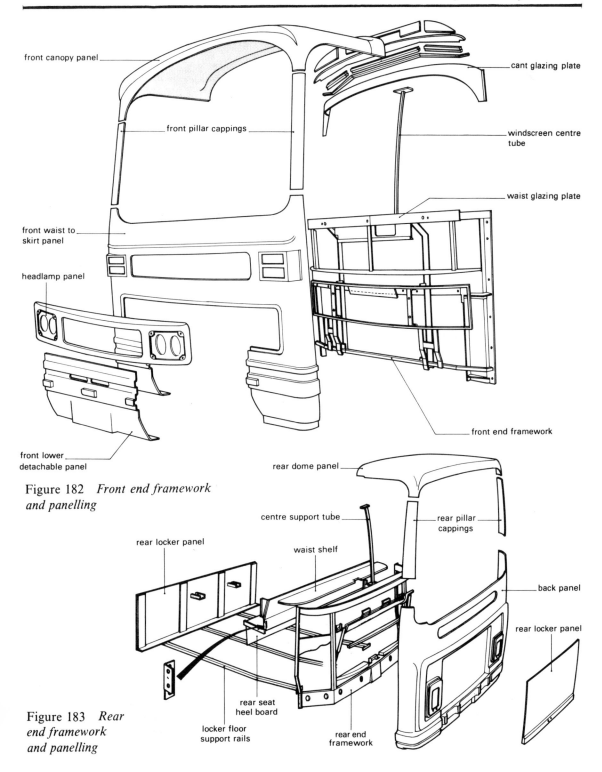

front canopy panel

cant glazing plate

front pillar cappings

windscreen centre tube

waist glazing plate

front waist to skirt panel

headlamp panel

front end framework

front lower detachable panel

Figure 182 *Front end framework and panelling*

rear dome panel

centre support tube

rear pillar cappings

rear locker panel

waist shelf

back panel

rear locker panel

rear seat heel board

locker floor support rails

rear end framework

Figure 183 *Rear end framework and panelling*

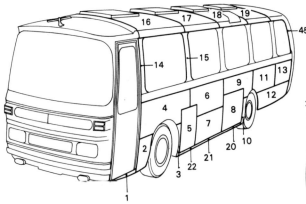

Figure 184   *Panel descriptions for 10-m long luxury coach (see text for key)*

The exterior panelling arrangement for a 10-m coach body is shown in Figure 184. The various parts are as follows:

1   Entrance doorway skirt panel
2   Skirt panel front of front N/S wheel-arch
3   Skirt panel rear of front N/S wheel-arch
4   N/S main side panel, Bay 1
5   Air filter access flap
6   N/S main side panel, Bay 2
7   Skirt panel
8   Spare wheel access flap
9   N/S main side panel, Bay 3
10   Skirt panel front of rear N/S wheel-arch
11   N/S main side panel, Bay 4
12   Rear skirt panel, N/S
13   N/S main side panel, Bay 5
14   Pillar capping between Bay 1 and entrance door
15   Pillar cappings main pillars
16   Roof panel, Bay 1
17   Roof panel, Bay 2
18   Roof panel, Bay 3
19   Roof panel, Bay 4
20   Valance panel for spare wheel access flap
21   Valance panel
22   Valance panel for air filter access flap
23   Front skirt panel, O/S
24   Main side panel below driver's signalling window, O/S
25   O/S main side panel, Bay 1
26   Skirt panel rear of front O/S wheel-arch
27   O/S brake gear access flap

28   Valance panel for O/S brake gear access flap
29   Valance panel
30   O/S main side panel, Bay 2
31   Skirt panel front of rear O/S wheel-arch
32   O/S main side panel, Bay 3
33   O/S rear skirt panel
34   O/S main side panel, Bay 4
35   Main side panel below emergency door
36   Emergency door main side panel
37   Pillar capping between emergency door and Bay 4
38   Emergency door, top rail capping
39   Emergency door, shut pillar capping
40   Emergency door, hinge pillar capping
41   Water bottle flap
42   Fuel filler flap
43   Header tank flap (not shown)
44   Electrical flap
45   N/S rear pillar capping
46   O/S No. 1 pillar capping

The main roof panels are aluminium with moulded glass-fibre dome and canopy panels, while body panels below the waist line are aluminium at the sides and glass fibre at the front and rear.

Glass-fibre-reinforced plastics work

Design considerations

GRP is used structurally and thereby is often in competition with metal. The materials are so dissimilar that a quite different design approach is desirable for each. Whereas metals are homogeneous and isotropic, GRP is a resin continuum in which glass fibres are incorporated as strength members. Within wide limits, strength is proportional to glass content.

The fibres may be randomly distributed (as in mats) or aligned to give orientation of strength (as in rovings and woven fabric).

The cost of the resin and glass is higher than low-carbon steel, but mat and resin unmoulded is roughly equivalent to aluminium on a volume basis. The design rules which make for the best use of the material are as follows:

1 Make use of the ease of forming to compound curvature to give added stiffness to the structure.
2 Where panels require local strength and stiffness, use local thickening only or mould in, for example, ribs, hollow sections, or lightweight cores.
3 Design so that the structure can be moulded in as few pieces as possible. This saves fabrication costs and eliminates a source of stress concentration.
4 Use well radiused curves where possible. This assists in obtaining good fibre distribution and makes for ease of air removal.
5 Give as much taper as possible to deep mouldings and avoid undercuts. This facilitates ease of removal from the mould.
6 Consider GRP-to-metal attachment points carefully – particularly where shear and bearing loads are involved. Spread the loads by using washers, metal inserts, etc.
7 Bear in mind that stress concentrations are not relieved by yielding as they are in ductile materials.
8 The loads that a moulding will withstand are, as with other materials, dependent on time and environment.

Hand lay-up technique

This is the most popular method of making 'shell structures' such as vehicle panels. The advantages are that equipment and mould costs are at a minimum while stiffening framework or attachment brackets can readily be moulded into the body of the laminate. Disadvantages are that the quality of the part depends greatly on the skill of the moulder. With most polyester resins, draughts across the lay-up or temperatures below 15°–18°C can lead to undercure while too strong heating before resin gelation can result in blistering and delamination. With care and reasonable facilities, however, good results can be achieved and structures made which would be very difficult to match with other methods. A reasonably rigid, smooth-surfaced mould is required and may be of reinforced plastics material, metal or, if adequately sealed to make the surface impervious, of wood or plaster. Due to the requirement of a good outer finish on vehicles, a female mould is generally used. Female moulds are frequently produced by moulding on a well-finished plaster or wooden mock-up.

Having made the mould, it is coated with a release agent which may be a hard wax, a film former, such as polyvinyl alcohol (PVA) or a proprietary preparation. A two-stage system is often used, e.g. wax followed by PVA. Where the moulded surface is later to be painted, film formers are preferable to wax alone.

Mouldings have a better finish if the surfaces are resin-rich and this is conveniently achieved by

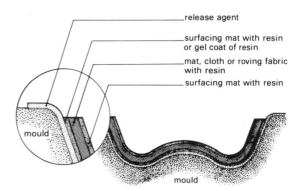

release agent

surfacing mat with resin or gel coat of resin

mat, cloth or roving fabric with resin

surfacing mat with resin

mould

mould

Figure 185 *GRP moulding*

using surfacing mat as the first and final layers (see Figure 185). While the proportion of glass in the surfaces will be low, it confers stability and craze resistance and since by its use it is unnecessary to let the resin gel before proceeding with the lay-up, time is saved and 'gel coat' wrinkling avoided.

The activated resin, which may contain a thixotropic filler to prevent drainage on inclined surfaces, and may be pigmented if desired, is brushed, sprayed, or applied with a paint roller to the release-agent-coated mould surface. Surfacing mat is laid into it and air removed with a disc roller. Further resin is then applied and the reinforcement material laid in position. For most vehicle bodywork applications this will be chopped strand mat but where cost is secondary to strength a woven fabric is used. With mat, the resin tends to come up through it and bring out entrapped air as rolling proceeds. The resin dissolves the mat binder and filament size and after a short time springiness is lost and the strands 'bed down' and knit together at lapped or butted joints. Further layers of mat are added as necessary without waiting for gelation and then the layer of surfacing mat applied to give a fine grain finish to the unmoulded surface. With woven rovings fabric or yarn cloth as reinforcement, the resin can be applied by pre-dipping if desired but air has still to be removed from between layers. With cloth mouldings, a squeegeeing technique is preferable to rolling, the air being eased towards the open edge of the lay-up.

Until several identical mouldings have been made and a time allocated, it is best to allow a generous pot life when activating the resin, so permitting the moulding to be cured as one piece. Polyester resins are activated in cold-curing by adding to them in turn a catalyst, which may be a liquid, paste or powder, and a liquid 'accelerator'. On no account should the catalyst and accelerator be mixed together. Cure can be effected in a few minutes to many hours depending on the amounts of activators added and the temperature conditions. The temperature build up in thick sections by the exothermic curing reaction of the resin can be such as to cause blisters or delamination; in these cases it is best to allow heat

to dissipate by phased curing. In all cases, it is important that the gelation time is sufficiently long for the mat binder to have been dissolved by the resin and for all entrapped air to have been worked out. On the other hand a very prolonged gelation time increases the risk of styrene monomer evaporation and so of incomplete curing. Care should be taken that mouldings are not strained if removed from the mould before they are completely hard. This applies particularly to lay-ups on male formers since the small resin shrinkage will cause contraction on to the mould.

By the contact moulding method, chopped strand mat laminates usually have a resin/glass ratio by weight of between 2:1 and 3:1, medium weight cloth laminates a ratio of 2:3 and roving fabric laminates 1:1.

Joining mouldings

Joints in GRP can be made satisfactorily by bonding, riveting, bolting and frequently by screwing. Where possible, however, the parts should be designed and moulded as one piece to utilize the strength of the glass fibres. Bonding can be carried out with polyester or epoxide resins. It is preferable to roughen the surfaces to be bonded and to have the 'glue line' in shear rather than tension, i.e. by lapping rather than butting. Riveting is best done with soft aluminium or copper rivets and should not be less than $2\frac{1}{2}$ hole diameters from the edges of the parts. Bolting requires the same consideration as riveting in regard to distance from the edge of the part. Again, $2\frac{1}{2}$ diameters should be allowed between bolts in a line for maximum efficiency in tension.

Machining

GRP is abrasive but can be quite satisfactorily machined. Carbide tipped tools are recommended. Sawing is best done with abrasive discs although high-speed metal blades with widely spaced, coarse, offset teeth are satisfactory. For 'one-off' mouldings, sawing and edge trimming can be done with tools normally used for metal or wood. Sanding is generally employed to finish rough edges. Grinding presents no particular difficulties and standard coolants are used. Grinding discs on flexible drives are sometimes used for edge trimming.

Drilling requires care to avoid delamination of cloth mouldings. Tapping is not recommended unless for lightly loaded connections. Coarse threads are preferred to fine. Shearing, punching and blanking are satisfactory with sharp tools.

Painting

Many moulded GRP parts can with advantage incorporate pigments so that the necessity for painting is avoided.

Where painting is required, all traces of mould release agent must first be removed and it is advisable to sand the part with medium grit paper. Undercured mouldings and those with air voids near the surface can allow the paint to sink after a period. Experience is that synthetic paints or hot-sprayed cellulose are preferable to air-drying cellulose. The use of coarse woven cloth on the surface of a moulding will often be revealed by a weave pattern, although this may not be unattractive in some instances.

Repair of mouldings

Damage is generally localized and confined to small cracks or fractures. In this case broken material should be removed and the edges feathered. Loose chopped strands, mat, or either combined with fabric, should be laid into the cavity and impregnated with activated resin. Filler may be added to prevent drainage on inclined surfaces and a further layer, bonding on to the moulding at least 25 mm beyond the damaged area, is desirable for heavy duty mouldings. Cellulose film, adhered at the edges with tape, is a useful backing for the patch and may be applied to the surface also to exert some pressure and to lessen the amount of buffing necessary.

Ventilation, heating and demisting

An improvement in the method of coach body ventilation has been the development of the spot vent system, which avoids the frequent irritation caused to passengers by opened windows. This is particularly important on long-distance coaches on Continental tours, where high ambient temperatures require considerable forced ventilation for passenger comfort.

The system of spot ventilation using ball-type ventilators has been used for many years on ships, aircraft and railcars with decided advantages, but it had been found difficult to apply the method to road vehicles due to the size and load of the blower units required to make the system effective and the high pressures required with many ventilator units. Installed in luxury touring coaches are efficient ducting systems which incorporate a blower unit of sufficient high power and low electrical load to meet the requirements of PSV operation. In addition, specially developed ventilators known as 'jet vents' have been produced which have a low pressure differential to keep the blower loading to a minimum.

This system is attractive to bodybuilders and operators in that it provides a means for completely or partially fixing the glazing throughout the vehicle length, in addition to ensuring a standard of passenger ventilation that can be controlled by the individual without irritation to other passengers. Air is drawn into the vehicle through a forward-facing intake mounted on the coach roof with blowers mounted in the roof ducting to feed air to the adjustable 'jet vents' under pressure. The air is then emitted from the vent nozzles at fairly high velocity as required by the passenger. The air is neither heated nor cooled and a separate saloon heating system of conventional type is employed for use during cold weather.

Natural ventilation

Natural ventilation is a suitable name for air circulation not using a blower but only ram (or dynamic) pressure on the outside of the vehicle. Many different openings can be used as air intakes: hinged flaps, scoops, rotating ventilators. As a general rule, inlets should be in positions of high positive pressure on the vehicle body surface where they are not exposed to the ingress of dust and mud. Outlets should be clearly placed at areas of low pressure so that no impurities can be sucked in.

Air-conditioning

Air-conditioning units include cooling and humidity control facilities as well as temperature control and air-circulation. The typical air-conditioning unit takes air from the outside and inside of the vehicle body. After cleaning in an air filter, the air flows through a heat exchanger, where it is either warmed or cooled. The air stream is subjected to wetting or drying according to the humidity requirements. Control of most air conditions is automated so that the driver has only to manipulate a few controls.

Demisting and heating equipment

Two units are usually provided at the front end, one each side, connecting up to the demister nozzles at the bottom of the windscreen and also to outlets at floor level giving heating and ventilation for driver and front passengers. These units are fitted with temperature control to give fresh air intake from hot to cold depending on climatic conditions. In addition one, two or three under-seat recirculator heaters can be fitted.

Windows

Some coachbuilders are using the direct glazing system of window glass retention instead of the rubber gasket method which has been in existence for many years. Direct glazing is an adhesive system which replaces the rubber gasket or glazing rubber section and still maintains the 'resilient' cushion-like securement. The advantages of direct glazing include:

1 A reduction on leakage.
2 Adhesive glazing increases torsional stiffness of the body, the glass functioning as a structural member together with the body pillars and rails and contributing substantially to the body strength.

3 Due to this contribution by the glass, it is possible to reduce the thickness of surrounding framework without loss of strength, thus enabling the stylist to concentrate on greater visibility by substituting for the thick rubber gasket a slim trim strip. This makes the vehicle much more attractive.
4 There is strong evidence to support the contention that fewer breakages occur, due to the fact that the glass is allowed to remain in its natural alignment when directly bonded, without tension points being created by the pull of the gasket. It is not recommended that darkened or reflecting glass side windows should be used because this prevents passengers from taking photographs from the coach.

Painting

The painting of motor vehicles is carried out for a number of reasons:

1 Since most materials are affected by the atmosphere, a protective coat will reduce corrosion and rotting.
2 Vehicle bodies are subjected to a variety of conditions ranging from rain, snow, grit, salt and sea spray and industrial chemical atmospheres, so the hard-wearing surfaces produced by many modern finishes are essential.
3 The appearance of a vehicle is usually improved and commercial vehicles are more noticeable when painted in a firm's or operator's distinctive colours.

Construction methods and the materials used in the building of modern road vehicles have been subject to such rapid development and improvement during recent years that many operations, once so essential in producing a first-class coach finish, have become superfluous. Filling and stopping is now substantially reduced and fewer coats of paint are needed so that the finishing operation has become progressively simpler and more economical. Even so, in view of the present-day high cost of running a vehicle or fleet of vehicles, the operator is always seeking for even more economical painting schedules both in respect of painters' time and cost of materials, while he is only too well aware that the longer his vehicle is off the road, the more revenue it is failing to earn.

In the field of paint technology, advances have also been made and new resins, oils and pigments have been developed which have been combined to produce products with better build, speedier drying and enhanced durability so that the specialist manufacturer of coach and vehicle finishes can now offer the bodybuilder or fleet operator a range of materials and processes which will exactly suit the requirements and the budget of the user. These materials can be utilized for the initial painting of a new body or for the routine maintenance of fleet vehicles.

It is of vital importance that surfaces which are to be painted should receive thorough preparation and pretreatment. However high the quality of the paint, unless the adhesion of the primer to the substrate is good, then the paint film is virtually unsupported and breakdown is inevitable. This takes the form of peeling, flaking, cracking or blistering. Not only does this mean that refinishing has to be undertaken much earlier than antici-pated, but, in addition, the refinishing process is made very much more difficult through the necessity of having to strip the old paint process, right back to bare metal again. It is false economy to ignore or skimp the surface preparation.

Examples of painting schedules are given in Figure 186.

Paintshop safety

The following rules should be followed to ensure safety in the paint shop:

1 Display 'No Smoking' and 'No Naked Flames' and ensure that blow lamps or welding equipment are not used in the immediate vicinity of the painting area.
2 Fire extinguishers of the correct type should be placed in prominent positions and all personnel should be made aware of their location. These extinguishers must be serviced regularly.
3 All electrical equipment must be correctly earthed and all solvent containers should conform to the appropriate regulations. Never use temporary electrical set-ups.

Operation	Six-coat process	Four-coat process	Three-coat process	Three-coat process	Two-coat process
1	pretreatment				
2	primer	primer	primer	intercoat	intercoat
3	intercoat	intercoat	intercoat	enamel	enamel
4	enamel	enamel	enamel	signwriting, lining and transfers	signwriting, lining and transfers
5	enamel	signwriting, lining and transfers	signwriting, lining and transfers	body varnish	
6	flatting varnish	body varnish			
7	signwriting, lining and transfers				
8	body varnish				
	de-luxe process for new work	economical process for new work	minimum process for new work	recommended for repaints	low-cost emergency process for repaints
					intercoat on replacement panels, one coat of enamel over all

Figure 186 *Schedule of finishing processes*

4   Avoid spontaneous combustion by putting all dirty rags, papers and empty paint tins into covered containers, which must be cleared from the paint shop at the end of every shift.

5   Provide a good ventilation and extraction system, to prevent dangerous concentration of vapours and to avoid paint over-spray. Precautions must be taken against the inhalation of fumes, dust or spray by the correct use of a face mask or a respirator.

6   The engines of vehicles should not be started in or near to the paint shop but should be moved by hand.

7   Replace the lids of part-used containers immediately after use.

8   Keep the whole area including the floors clean. Spillage of thinners or paint can produce very slippery and dangerous conditions.

9   Take a careful note of any special instructions regarding the handling and use of materials which the manufacturer may highlight, either on the containers or in the literature.

10   All personnel who handle or use paint and thinners must wear overalls, gloves and goggles wherever possible, and barrier cream should be used to protect exposed areas of the skin.

17 Vehicle inspection check

To ensure smooth operation and a high-quality completed vehicle, a thorough inspection should be carried out before the vehicle is delivered to the operator or dealer. The following summarizes major points. Check and ensure that:

1 No wiring has become accidentally disconnected or has been trapped or damaged during the course of body mounting. Any additional wiring fitted should be adequately protected and clipped into position.

2 Brake pipes have not been trapped or accidentally bent or flattened during the course of body or equipment mounting.

3 Wheel-arch clearance dimension is at least the minimum recommended for the vehicle.

4 All body-mounting brackets are secure and the spacing is at least as recommended for the type of body involved.

5 On a chassis where 'U' bolts are allowed, the steel spacers are firmly in position and secure and no distortion of the frame side member flanges has occurred during fitment and tightening of the 'U' bolts.

6 PTO controls are located in the manner recommended by the chassis manufacturer.

7 Any relocated or additional fuel lines are adequately clipped to prevent sagging and are protected from damage. Also ensure there is adequate clearance between the fuel lines and other chassis components.

8 On chassis fitted with tilt cabs, the cab can be tilted without fouling bodywork or any special equipment that has been fitted. The cab does not trap or become fouled by any bodywork or equipment or equipment controls when the cab is locked in position. Tilting or securing of the cab does not foul or trap any brake connections or electrical wiring.

9 Cab gap to body or centre-line of front axle to body is such that, at the GVW, the resultant axle loadings are within those recommended for the vehicle.

10 Clearances for any additional piping that has been fitted are in line with those recommended by the chassis manufacturer.

11 No holes have been drilled in the chassis frame side member flanges and no welding to the frame has taken place for the mounting of the bodywork or equipment.

12 When drilling new holes in the chassis frame web, there are no more than two in a vertical plane. The distance between the holes is not less than twice the diameter of the rivets or bolts used and any holes drilled are not less than the specified distance from the edge of the frame.

13 Engine air cleaner intake is not obstructed by bodywork or equipment and the clearance to air cleaner system is not less than the minimum specified by the chassis manufacturer.

14 All electrical equipment functions satisfactorily. Check by switching on all lamps, flasher indicators, panel lights and warning system lamps. Lights should be left on for sufficient time to check that overheating of wiring looms is not occurring as this would result in a wiring burn-up.

15 All rear lights, reflectors, stop lights and direction indicators conform in location to legal requirements, particularly where elec-

trical equipment has been relocated due to fitting of body or equipment.

16 Where the Special Vehicle Order Departments of chassis manufacturers have granted approval to the mounting of any bodywork or special equipment, any special points specified as a condition of the approval have been followed.

18 Examination questions

Questions 1-30 are taken from recent papers set for the City and Guilds of London Institute examinations.

1 (a) Explain *five* significant design objectives which must be considered when mounting bodywork on special approval transit chassis windshield/van floor units.

   (b) Make a simple sketch to show how the following components of the floor to side assembly should be arranged to meet the design requirements of this type of vehicle:
   (i)   van floor panel
   (ii)   body side pillar
   (iii) body side rail
   (iv)   longitudinal reinforcing channel
   (v)   sideframe/floor frame attachment bracket.

2 (a) Explain the advantages of using plywood in preference to tongue-and-groove boards for vehicle body flooring.

   (b) Explain the significant factors that determine the thickness of plywood to be used for body flooring applications.

   (c) Sketch and describe briefly a plywood-decked platform body side rail construction which makes provision for sign-writing along its length.

3 Specify the conditions which must be satisfied when the 'U' bolt and clip type of fastening is used for body to chassis mounting.

4 Explain the significant design features of *each* of the following commercial vehicle structures:
   (a) Separate body and chassis.
   (b) Semi-integral.
   (c) Integral.

5 Draw, full-size, *two* orthographic views showing an application of a flexible body mounting. Label the parts of the mounting and the adjacent body and chassis details.

6 A standard pressed-steel transit van is to be converted to provide an elevated roof:
   (a) Explain the design factors that must be considered to ensure that the conversion does not reduce the strength and serviceability of the vehicle.
   (b) Draw simple sketches to illustrate the additional framework, reinforcement, method of attachment, finishing and sealing.

7 Exterior plywood meets many of the needs of the vehicle bodybuilder and repairer due to its high two-way strength and wide range of surface finishes available.
   (a) State *five* of the surface finishes available.
   (b) State how the best results are obtained when machining plywood by (i) spindle moulding, (ii) drilling, (iii) routing, (iv) circular sawing.

8 *(a)* Explain *four* principal advantages of using aluminium for commercial vehicle body construction.

(b) Give *three* forms in which aluminium alloys are available for use in vehicle body construction. State *one* typical application in each case.

Type 1: Tongue and groove	Type 2: Lap joint		Type 3: Plank and capping section	Type 4: Corrugated
	A (plain)	B (hooked)		

Figure A *Planking sections*

9 Figure A shows examples of extruded aluminium alloy planking sections commonly used in vehicle body building. Compare in tabulated form their characteristics in terms of:

(a) Assembly.

(b) Performance under load concentrated on one plank.

(c) Water tightness.

(d) Ease of repair.

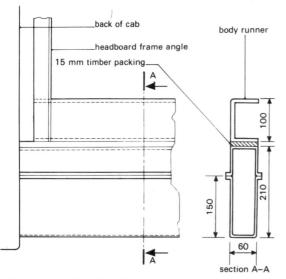

Figure B *Details of boxed chassis side frame member (dimensions in millimetres)*

10 Figure B shows details of a boxed-type chassis sideframe member and adjacent bodywork of a light dropside platform lorry. Sketch two orthographic views of a mounting arrangement which holds down the body and provides an anchorage for the headboard frame angle. Add brief notes, giving information relating to the materials used, treatment and fastenings.

11 Explain and illustrate the purpose of the following items used in the construction of commercial vehicle bodywork. Show how and where these items can be employed, stating in each case suitable materials and pre-treatment.

(a) Flitch plate.

(b) Truss panel.

(c) Gusset plate.

(d) Brace.

12 *(a)* Describe a method of insulating the different areas of a forward control driver's cab of a goods vehicle against excessive heat and noise. Specify the materials suitable for this purpose, making special reference to their essential properties.

(b) Make labelled sketches showing where these materials would be fitted and state how they would be secured.

13 A standard type of fixed-sided platform lorry body is mounted on a chassis which is designed to flex and weave.

(a) Discuss the effects of positioning deep timber body runners directly on top of the chassis frame side members and fastening by means of 'U' bolts.

(b) With the aid of a simple sketch, show a more satisfactory method of body mounting.

14 In accordance with current body and equipment mounting recommendations for goods vehicles, designed to ensure smooth operation and a high standard of quality, identify and explain briefly ten major items which should be checked by the bodybuilder or equipment installer before a completed vehicle is delivered to the operator or dealer.

15 *(a)* Draw appropriate wing travel opening sequences (closed, half open and fully open) for *each* of the following types of passenger service vehicle door:
   (i) Four wing double-folding inward-opening.
   (ii) Flush fitting two wing inward-opening glider.
   (iii) Two wing outward-opening contoured glider.
   (iv) 'Two plus one' folding/gliding combination.
(b) Explain briefly *four* safety features built into power-operated door systems for passenger vehicles.
(c) Sketch the layout of a pneumatic shelf-plate mechanism for double folding door operation.

16 *(a)* Make labelled sketches to show in correct sequence, the installation stages of a 'Huckbolt' type fastener used in all-metal body construction.
(b) Explain the performance characteristics of this type of structural fastener.

17 *(a)* Describe a five-point system of body mounting designed to allow a rigidly constructed tanker to float on the chassis so that flexibility is not affected.
(b) Sketch and label a frame outrigger mounting point which meets the design requirements of the mounting system.

18 Describe a typical rear end and closure detail of a Luton-type pantechnicon van body mounted on a 3.4-m wheelbase chassis cab. The van should be suitable for furniture removal requirements and offer two optional extras or alternatives for customer approval.

19 Specify *five* significant design and construction objectives which must be satisfied when

bodywork conversions are carried out on standard production van units, so that the conversion does not reduce the strength and serviceability of the vehicle.

20 *(a)* **Outline the advantages which the demountable body system offers management and operators in the transportation segment of distribution.**
(b) **Summarize the significant engineering features which govern demountable performance.**
(c) **Describe in correct sequence the mounting procedure.**

21 *(a)* Draw to a scale of one-tenth full size, an elevation showing the inside face of the framing for an inward-opening single front entrance door of a luxury touring coach. Indicate the overall dimensions of the door and add brief notes relating to the material used and the method of construction.
(b) Make labelled sketches to show the positioning of the upper and lower pivot arrangement which would permit the door to swing inwards to suit the requirements shown in Figure C.
(c) Sketch and label the main details of the interior pull handle and locking device. Indicate its position on the door.

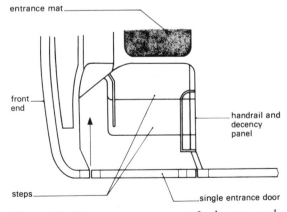

entrance mat

front end

handrail and decency panel

steps

single entrance door

Figure C   *Entrance arrangement for luxury coach body*

22 Make pictorial sketches in good proportion, to show *each* of the following assemblies of a Luton-type van body constructed from standard extruded aluminium alloy sections:
 (a) Front cross-bearer, assembly to bulkhead pillar and panel, front floor angle, chassis and mounting.
 (b) Cross-bearer, assembly to main side pillar, floor stringer, gusset and floor planking.
 (c) Add brief notes giving information relating to the method of fastening and the condition of the material used.

23 (a) Describe *two* structural weaknesses of timber which are overcome by its manufacture into plywood.
 (b) Explain fully the meaning of the abbreviation WBP used in conjunction with plywood.

24 (a) State two factors which determine the cross-bearer spacings in a fixed-sided platform body.
 (b) Explain briefly why a fishplate is sometimes used as a substitute for an outrigger bracket.

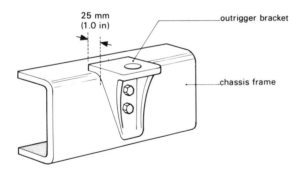

Figure D *Outrigger bracket detail*

 (c) Explain briefly how the outrigger bracket shown in Figure D assists in *(i)* relieving the bolts of shear stress, and *(ii)* transmitting the bodyload to the web of the chassis.

25 Sketch in good proportion a sectional view through the chock rail (side rave) and sideboard of a general purpose truck body constructed from standard aluminium alloy extrusions. The view must show:
 (a) The method of fixing the chock rail to the cross-bearer.
 (b) A portion of the flooring.
 (c) A hinged and detachable drop sideboard.
 (d) The sideboard hinging arrangement.

26 Write a brief history of the motor car since the days of the 'horseless' carriage outlining the factors that led to the development of body engineering.

27 Describe, using labelled sketches, how the following major assemblies of an integral car body are designed to counteract the various stresses to which they are subjected:
 (a) Underbody.
 (b) Roof.
 (c) Body side.

28 Describe, for a typical saloon car, how *each* of the following components of aerodynamic drag contribute to the total resistance to motion:
 (a) Profile drag.
 (b) Induced drag.
 (c) Frictional resistance.
 (d) Interference drag.
 (e) Cooling system drag.

29 (a) Define the following styles of passenger car body: *(i)* coupé, *(ii)* limousine, *(iii)* estate.
 (b) List *six* distinctive groups of passenger car body.

30 Describe a typical isothermal van body side frame of all-metal construction. Specify the essential characteristics relating to *each* of the following:
 (a) Main side pillars.
 (b) Insulation.
 (c) Panel joints.
 (d) Completed side frame.

Index